Preparing Your Team for FLL™ Competition

by

K.K. Quah

All inquires should be addressed to

K.K. Quah
Email: kkquah@tlck.com
http://www.tlck.com

ISBN 1-933359-08-0

Cover and logo designed by Scott Fleming

Forward

3...2...1... LEGO®! At FLL™ tournaments throughout the world LEGO® MINDSTORMS® robots bolt out of base the way thoroughbreds race out of a starting gate.

If you have been a coach, parent or team member at an FLL™ tournament, you know the intense thrill as your finely engineered robot jumps out of base at the start of a 2 1/2 minute match. If you are just starting out in FLL™, then you can look forward to an exhilaration and excitement that you can rarely experience anywhere else.

My introduction to FIRST® (For Inspiration and Recognition of Science and Technology) robotics began seven years ago when I attended a high school FIRST® Robotics championship at Kennedy Space Center in Titusville, Florida. My son, then 11-years-old, and I were overwhelmed by the boundless energy, enthusiasm and industry of the teams, coaches, spectators, referees and judges. How delighted we were to discover that an international robotics competition using LEGO® MINDSTORMS® was also offered by FIRST® to elementary and middle school students ages 9-14. I volunteered to be an FLL™ coach. During that first season, the students slowly ascended the moderately sloped learning curve of knowledge about the FLL concepts of project management, physics, programming, mathematics, teamwork, engineering and problem solving.

I say "moderately sloped" for two reasons. Although I always had great interest in these concepts, my education did not involve training in these areas (I am a physician and practice adult medicine). I was just able to keep us a step a head of the team in the technical areas of the challenge. Second, although I had intensely searched through libraries, Internet resources and bookstores, I could not find a manual or guide on how to present this information in a fun and entertaining manner.

How pleased I was to chance upon KK during a "pilgrimage" to the LEGO® Imagination Center in Downtown Disney, Florida. He was there offering a demonstration of his own robots and was the first person I knew of who was using this platform in my vicinity. I learned not only that KK offered an after school enrichment program that demonstrated engineering and robotic concepts using LEGO®, but he had published a workbook (Elementary Engineering 1) that presented his curriculum in a fun and engaging way that secretly "tricked" students into learning. I have used this workbook and its sequel Elementary Engineering 2 to teach dozens of children simple and compound machines and robotics with this unique hands-on approach and "challenges" during my own FLL™ training sessions and summer camps.

Through five years of FLL™ coaching, I have been privileged to share in KK's experience, observations and insights. I have applied most of the ideas contained in this book to my own FLL™ teams and have seem these teams master a deeper knowledge of engineering and problem-solving principles. There is a point in the journey of every FLL™ team where, after having built your first Tri-bot, completed the basic NXT-G™ tutorials and constructed all the mission models, you and your team say, "Now what?". The book you now hold, Preparing Your Team for First Lego League™, is a first-class answer to that question.

Congratulations to you and your team for deciding to participate in an innovative program that will build not only science and technology skills and interests, but self-confidence, leadership, and life skills. If you are a returning FLL™ coach, you'll gain valuable knowledge and practical ideas to advance your team's competence. If you are a new FLL™ coach, I know this manual will serve as a roadmap for you and your team to better experience the exhilaration at the start of your first FLL™ performance match, Three... -Two... -One... -LEGO®!

Paul Bresnan MD
Six-year veteran FLL™ coach
Two-year FLL™ World Festival Referee.

Contents   Page

Note: Details of topics covered for each camp day are found on pages 11 and 12.

Overview
of
FIRST®
LEGO®
League™

"There is always room for improvement."

Acknowledgements

Thanks to the following:

The LEGO® Group

The people at FIRST®

The people that work for FLL™ notably Scott Evans, etc. who do a fantastic job of running a world-class tournament every year

My fellow coaches who devote a lot of time to their teams

Tournament organizers and hosts, without whom the FLL™ tournament structure would not exist

Thanks to Mech Master Aaron Coutinho, who helped design the tension trigger

Special thanks to my friend, Paul Bresnan, whose tireless reviews have made this a better book

Materials Used in the Book

The lab kits used for this book are the education version of the NXT™, set 9797 and set 9648, and are available from www.LEGOEducation.com. We will be building a sample robot to help you see the process of developing a robotic platform, and using manipulators with that platform to help inspire creative development.

Conventions Used in the Book

The names of the LEGO® pieces used will employ the LDraw™ naming scheme. See the Appendix in the back for more information on LDraw™.

At times in the book we will be using Mission examples.   These are simply examples of actual prior FLL™ missions to illustrate how some mission was solved and the process that was involved in making the solution workable and eventually robust.

This represents the walls at the edges of a table.

This symbol represents a mission or target.

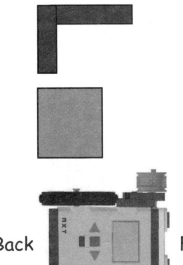

Back   Front

This symbol represents the robot.

Introduction

Short History of FLL™

First, there was FIRST®, which stands for For Inspiration and Recognition of Science and Technology. FIRST® was dedicated to using a robotics competition called FIRST® Robotics Competition (FRC) to help promote interest in science, technology, engineering and mathematics. It was founded by Dean Kamen and has held annual competitions since 1990. In 1998, FIRST® approached The LEGO® Group to see if they would be interested in holding robotic competitions using LEGO® MINDSTORMS®, released in September 1998. Things moved quickly and a pilot competition was planned for 1999. Thus was born the FIRST® LEGO® League (FLL™) which features a new theme each year for the 9-14 year age group.

FLL™ Today

Each year the competition has grown and the number of teams has mushroomed. In August 2006, The LEGO® Group introduced their new 32-bit platform for robotics called MINDSTORMS® NXT™, and during the 2006-7 season both the original MINDSTORMS® Robotics Invention System™ or RIS and the MINDSTORMS® NXT™ were jointly allowed for the FIRST® LEGO® League™ competition. It is likely that only the NXT™ will be allowed in future FLL™ events.

How to Use This Book

This book is intended for coaches, specifically new coaches who might be parents or teachers who have decided to form a robotics team and compete in FLL™.

I was a mentor for a team in 2001 and formed my own team, called Mech Masters, based in sunny Florida since 2002. During the years I have been a coach, I have helped inspire the formation of a few teams and have talked to numerous other parents about forming a team. One of the most common comments is a parent saying they are not "technical" enough to be a coach. At the World FLL™ Festivals in Atlanta during 2005-2008, I was a speaker and also heard such comments, and decided that I could write a book and hopefully inspire even more people to form teams. A coach does not have to have a lot of technical knowledge to guide the team, and in fact only basic knowledge of the workings of the NXT™ is necessary. Beyond that, it is a matter of guiding the team members only when needed and keeping things simple. On the other hand, I also understand the frustration of forming a team and not knowing how to get them ready. So use this as a training guide to get your team ready.

Veteran teams might still learn a thing or two about how to compete better in a very hard and complicated tournament. So use this as a resource or an idea book to inspire you with more solutions. In the FLL™ 2007-8 season, things have just started to get more complicated, and I always say, "When things get more complex, that is precisely the time that someone needs to step up and try to simplify things." So here is my two cents on it.

It is my sincerest hope that this book will help inspire more coaches to form teams that will take part in this wonderful activity.

What Is This Book About and Not About?

I will be concentrating on the "technical" side of the competition, so I will be talking a lot about robots and the manipulators and the problem solving that is involved in getting missions worked out.   There will be little to no discussion on the teamwork presentation and the research presentation.

This book is not about clever solutions for missions.   There are wonderful examples of creative solutions to missions, but I hope those are there for inspiration. With my team, I prefer to concentrate on learning skills and processes that the team members can apply to any problem. There are no "magic bullets", and solutions used one year on a mission are likely not appropriate for the missions the following year.

I hope to show you through this book that the FLL™ competition is NOT intimidating. I do hear how new coaches get overwhelmed by the number of rules the first year and are unsure about what to do and how to get their team ready. With this book as your guide, I hope you can see that it is very approachable and that keeping it simple does work.

All my team members know about simple machines (levers, wheels and axles, etc.) and they know about key mechanical concepts like gearing up and gearing down and the speed and torque trade-off.   They know about the principle of the pawl and ratchet, how to construct one, and how to apply ratchet mechanisms to appropriate areas.

They know how to approach a problem and make many improvements until an okay solution becomes a great solution.

Most importantly, I hope my team members learn the value of teamwork.   Practically all of the missions were solved by more than one person. I prefer to let teams of two kids solve a problem.   There are many times when a solution by a team member will be reworked by another member or many members to become the final, better solution.   These are the moments that I prize, because I believe this is one of the core learnings from an FLL™ tournament, i.e. that no one person can solve a problem well and it takes lots of work from many people.

In today's world, most technological solutions may require a person to see the current state of the solutions, then use that as a springboard for future improvements in conjunction with a team of people.   This helps promote teamwork.

Here's a story about keeping it simple.   At the State FLL™ for Mars Mission, my team scored 205 in Round 1 of the Robot Performance rounds, which we thought was great then.   Here we are five years later scoring 400 in Round 1 for State FLL™ for Power Puzzle and scores of 385 and 390 in subsequent rounds. We were the only team in Florida that registered a 400 points score in February 2008 at State FLL™.   We competed at the FLL™ International Open in Minneapolis, Minnesota in May 2008 and managed scores of 400, 370 and 400 in the opening day, and came away with the top spot in Robot Performance after the head-to-head sessions on the second day.

And we did it by keeping things simple. Our robot uses only two motors and virtually all our solutions are done with levers of some sort.   In fact, the simplicity meant that fewer things could go wrong, and if they did, it was easier to fix.

Overview of the FLL™ Competition

At its heart, FLL™ is about making kids want to learn science and mathematics. The competition with robots is the fun that attracts them to the subject. However, there are four portions to the tournament. Each team has a chance to score points in each of these categories and the overall top scores then determine the champion.

The four portions are:

Robot Performance (in which a team gets points for missions solved in 2.5 minutes),

Robot Design (a technical presentation to a panel of judges on the robot and manipulators used in mission solutions)

Research Presentation (a presentation of research done by the team on the theme of the tournament)

Teamwork Interview (which is usually a Q&A session, but may have a hands-on activity to test how well a team works together on problems)

There are typically local tournaments or qualifiers in which, if a team does well, they will qualify to advance to the State or Regional tournaments. Finally, if they are the champion at the State/Regional tournament, they may be able to advance to the World FLL™ Festival, which has taken place in Atlanta at the Georgia Dome and adjoining buildings in recent years.

Typical Schedule of an FLL™ Team

May 1	Registration begins for FLL™ season. Time to order materials.
early Sept.	Challenge is officially announced on-line.
mid Sept.	Registration closed.
Sept.-Feb.	Regular team meetings to work on all aspects of FLL™ Challenge.
Nov.-Feb.	Teams compete in local qualifiers and championship tournaments.
The following year	Qualified team competes in State/Regional FLL™ tournaments.
April following year	Invited teams compete in FLL™ World Festival (usually in Atlanta)

Team Meetings

How long each team meets varies on the needs of your team. My team usually meets on Saturdays from 9:30 am to 2:00 pm. About half the time is devoted to mission solutions and the other half to the research presentation. At the last few meetings, when we get closer to the tournaments, we start spending time talking through what team members will be demonstrating for the technical presentation in both the software side (programs are printed and put in a binder) and the hardware side (missions with interesting manipulators). I typically run through some teamwork presentation exercise, and we quiz the team members on various aspects of the FLL™ values.

I usually get the best and most experienced builders on a robot even before the season starts, so that particular aspect is done ahead of time. We then devote most mission solutions to the design of manipulators and programming the solutions. However, sometimes the challenge field may necessitate a change to the robot design, as we do not know the missions before the season starts.

In summary, the season runs from early September to about the end of February of the following year. This commitment looks daunting to parents, but this is a worthwhile activity. The FLL™ Coaches' Handbook reports that meeting times vary from one hour a week to ten hours a week so we are in the middle with about 4.5 hours a week.

Team Meetings (continued)

It is a good idea to have some one-on-one sessions with all team members, and to prepare for this I try to give some feedback on areas that they have worked and where they might need to improve. I use a form for this which I have included in the Appendix. However, I try to keep the feedback very positive and use it as a motivational tool.

What Does It Take To Get A Team Started?

The entry barrier for FLL™ is very low. Most of it is having the commitment and time to work with a group of kids. It does take a lot of patience and some team management, as everyone is different and team dynamics will vary from year to year.

The Requirements Are:

Coach and assistant coaches (usually parents or teachers)
Team members (up to 10 kids, I usually have 6-10 on my team)

Budget for the 2007-8 FLL™ season

- Team registration fee: $200 USD
- FLL™ Field Setup Kit: $65 USD (includes mat and models for missions)
- FLL™ Robotics Set (use old RIS™ set or get new NXT™ set). This part can vary a lot, but the minimum retail set for NXT™ is $250 and the recommended FLL™ Robot NXT™ set is $325 USD.
Using the highest cost (worse case), the required items total $590 USD.

Recommended Items Are:

Table for practice (again this can vary a lot, from $70-$150). See the table specifications on the www.firstlegoleague.org web site. I had my table constructed so it pulls apart into three equal pieces but can latch together to form the 4 foot x 8 foot table. It was more portable this way, as it can easily be carried in my SUV
NXT™ Rechargeable battery ($50) plus AC Adapter ($23) from LEGO® Education
Tournament Entry Fees (qualifiers run about $45 and State may run about $75). I am always optimistic about making it to the State/Regional FLL™ tournaments
T-shirts (about $5- 10 per person plus parents and supporters)
Research Binder for Research Presentation (to document team research activities)
Technical Binder for Robot Design Presentation

Additional Useful Items:

These are typically items donated by parents.
Tri-fold display boards for team presentations
Team photos
Binders for presentations
All kinds of miscellaneous office supplies, tape, glue, etc.

Parents are asked to take turns on the snacks and lunch for the team. Travel expenses are usually also taken care of by respective parents. However, I do try to encourage car pooling to the meetings and to tournaments.

So let's get started getting the team ready!

<u>Week Long Camp Format</u>
I have found robotics can be nicely introduced in a week-long half-day camp - Mondays through Fridays from 9 am to 12 noon in a camp. The morning sessions typically involve more lecture and are followed by "challenges/problems" in the afternoons. The emphasis is on trying out things that are taught. Below are the topics covered each day and the suggested time to spend on each topic.

<u>Day 1:</u>	<u>Time (minutes)</u>
MINDSTORMS® NXT™ set and pieces	20
Menu Tree for NXT™ Intelligent Brick	5
Standard Port Settings for NXT™	5
Differential Drive System	5
Desirable Robot Features	10
Build BasicBot	25
Break.	15
Introduction to Programming BasicBot	25
Navigation Exercise 1 - Forwards/Backwards	10
Motor and Move Blocks	10
Navigation Exercise 2 - Turns	10
Rotation and Degrees in Navigation	10
Math with Angles	5
Use of View in Navigation	5
The Geometry of Turns	5
Use of Rotations vs. Timer	15

<u>Day 2:</u>	
Notes on Challenges, 3P	10
Typical Problem Solving Process in FLL™	10
Path, Program, Pieces	10
Shaped Manipulators	10
Robot Modifications	25
Break	10
General Rules for All Missions	10
Token Delivery Challenge	90
Lessons Learned	5

<u>Day 3:</u>	
Introduction to the Light Sensor	10
Light Sensor Exercise 1 - Basic Light Readings	10
Basic Loop Forever Block	5
Different Uses of Loops	5
Light Sensor Exercise 2 - Testing with Lines	5
Problems and Fixes for the Light Sensor	5
Light Sensor Exercise 3 - Edge Detection	5
Center of Gravity Based Manipulator	5
COG Manipulator Exercise	20
Break.	15
Multiple Retrieval Challenge	90
Lessons Learned	5

Day 4:

Introduction to the Ultrasonic Sensor	10
Ultrasonic Sensor Exercise - Distance Detection	10
Ultrasonic Sensor Exercise - Collision Detection	10
Switch Block	5
More Than One Condition	10
Problems and Fixes for the Ultrasonic Sensor	5
Lever Based Manipulator	10
Mechanics of Lever Based Manipulator	10
Break.	15
In the Hole Delivery Challenge	90
Lessons Learned	5

Day 5:

Introduction to the Sound Sensor	5
Sound Sensor Exercise - Basic Use	10
Introduction to the Touch Sensor	5
Touch Sensor Exercise - Basic Use	10
Tension Trigger Manipulator	10
Mechanics of a Tension Trigger Manipulator	10
Break	15
Hard To Reach Challenge	90
Lessons Learned	5
Summary of the Types of Missions	10
Summary of the Types of Manipulators	10

Introduction to Robotics Using NXT™

"The beginning is the most important part of the work." - Plato

Day 1
MINDSTORMS® NXT™ Set and Pieces
I will be concentrating on using the MINDSTORMS® NXT™ set for FLL™ competitions. However, teams using the older MINDSTORMS® RIS™ set are still permitted to use it for the FLL™ 2008-9 season.

The LEGO® MINDSTORMS® NXT™ robotics set was released in August 2006. The technology of processors, sensors, and even wiring, had all been upgraded in this robotics set. I remain convinced that this is a wonderful hobby robot set to introduce anyone to what robots can do.

The Brains of the Robot
The Intelligent Brick (IB) is the brains of the robot, found in the NXT™ set, which now sports a 32-bit microprocessor. The IB is where the input and output ports are located. Input ports are connection areas for a sensor on the IB to receive signals from sensors. There are four input ports on the IB (labeled 1, 2, 3 and 4).   The output ports are connection areas for devices to control typically motors.   There are three output ports on the IB (labeled A, B and C).

Intelligent Brick (IB)
The following buttons are used to operate the Intelligent Brick:
Square **Orange button** – press to switch on and as a select button.
Rectangular **Dark Gray button** – press to back up from a selection.
Triangular **Right and Left Arrow buttons** – press to choose different selection.

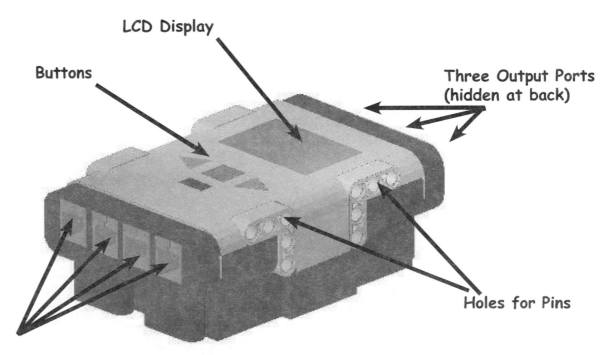

LCD Display

Buttons

Three Output Ports
(hidden at back)

Holes for Pins

Four Input Ports

Copyright © 2008 Technology Learning Classes for Kids

Connecting Wires and Wiring Management

The new connecting wires in NXT™ are proprietary and are thicker so that the wires are less flexible. This means the wires might get in the way of things so you need to make room somewhere on your model to be sure there is no interference with wheels or manipulators. This is an issue you need to keep in mind when working with the NXT™ robot.

Sensors

The NXT™ sets comes bundled with the light sensor, the touch sensor, the ultrasonic sensor and the sound sensor. A light sensor is a device that can sense between light, dark and color values and send out a signal to the robot brain. A touch sensor is a device that can send a signal to the robot brain when it has been triggered or bumped.

The ultrasonic sensor is a device which allows the robot to send out ultrasonic signals to calculate the distance to an object. This in effect allows an NXT™ robot to behave with a bat's echo-location ability. The sound sensor is a device that allows the robot to act or react upon hearing a sound above the threshold set by the sensor. For instance, you can make a robot move only when you clap or shout loudly enough.

| NXT™ Light Sensor | NXT™ Touch Sensor | NXT™ Sound Sensor | NXT™ Ultrasonic Sensor |

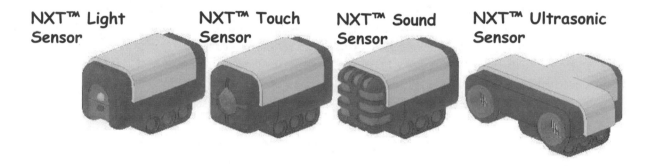

Sensors send signals back to the robot to help it to understand the environment. Special connecting wires are used to connect sensors to the input ports on the Intelligent Brick.

The shapes of the sensors underwent major changes. However, I believe the old touch sensor to be in some ways superior as it had a more compact design and the ability to attach it in different ways allowed for more flexible uses. Older sensors can still be utilized if you use a special connecting wire which has an adapter to the old style "2x2 brick" connection.

New Motor - Interactive Servo Motors

The new motors are large and have a rotation sensor built into them which give it an accuracy of one degree of angle of rotation detected. The new motors are at least 12 studs/bumps long and have a very irregular shape. Orient the motor as pictured with the bulky part downwards when building a model so that programming a robot to go forward will spin the motor in the correct direction. The motor may be at an angle. Note that if you reverse the orientation so that the bulky part of the motor is above, then a forward program block will actually move the robot backwards using default settings.

New Pieces and New Ways of Building

There are many new pieces in the NXT™ set. They are still Technic™ pieces. However, most of the pieces are Technic™ Beams or Technic™ Liftarms, 1xN Straight. In the older sets, there were a lot of bricks with holes of the type 1xN where N was an even number. However, the liftarms in NXT™ do not have studs/bumps on the top or sides. These beams/liftarms are distinguished by the number of holes, which are typically odd.

Why mostly odd numbers? Because in this case, it is easier to identify the middle point (hole) of an beam/liftarm and build from the middle to get a symmetrical model.

With the new pieces comes a new "design philosophy" which has been dubbed "studless building", which means it relies less on using studs and couplings at the tops and bottoms of bricks to hold pieces together. Instead it relies on pins and other connectors to hold the robot model together and function. Some people who have gotten used to the older philosophy have a little more trouble making the adjustment. However, regardless of the new studless building philosophy, there is no limitation on what can be used at the FLL™ competition. My team still uses many older Technic™ pieces to come up with creative solutions to missions.

I have the naming convention of some of the new NXT™ pieces in the Appendix to help teams to become familiar with the pieces. Some names do get awkward in the LDraw™ naming convention, and for those I do try to simplify, as long as all team members are aware of how that piece is referenced. It is important that we are not confused when referring to parts. This is important, because engineers in real life have standard definitions for parts, which help them communicate concepts and also avoid mistakes in discussing projects.

Once you switch on the Intelligent Brick (IB), it's time to get to know your way around the menu and the various functions of the IB.

Menu Tree for NXT™ Intelligent Brick

When you first switch on the IB, you hear a tune and see the My Files icon.
Keep pressing the right arrow button; you will see the following cycle through the LCD panel:
NXT™ Program - View - Bluetooth - Settings - Try Me - My Files.

From My Files, if you press the orange button, you will see Software Files.
Keep pressing the right arrow button and you will see the following cycle:
NXT™ Files, Sound Files, Software Files

From Software Files, if you press the orange button, you will see your programs.
Press once to select the program to run or right/left arrow to select other programs to run.
Then press the orange button again to run the program.

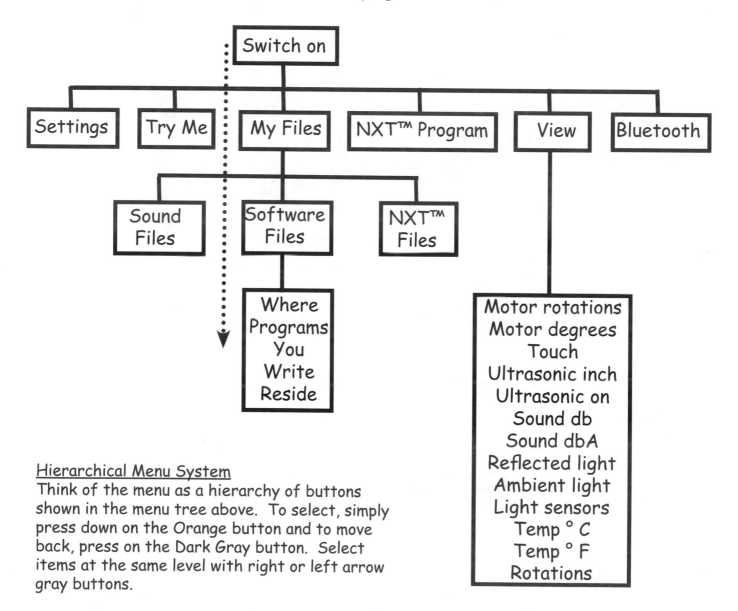

Hierarchical Menu System
Think of the menu as a hierarchy of buttons shown in the menu tree above. To select, simply press down on the Orange button and to move back, press on the Dark Gray button. Select items at the same level with right or left arrow gray buttons.

Standard Port Settings for Sensors and Motors

One of the first things to learn is how to connect the motors and sensors to the IB. The standard ports to use are:

Input Ports
Port 1 - Touch Sensor
Port 2 - Sound Sensor
Port 3 - Light Sensor
Port 4 - Ultrasonic Sensor

Output Ports
Port A - Motor used for extra function (for example, a motorized manipulator)
Port B - Motor for movement
Port C - Motor for movement

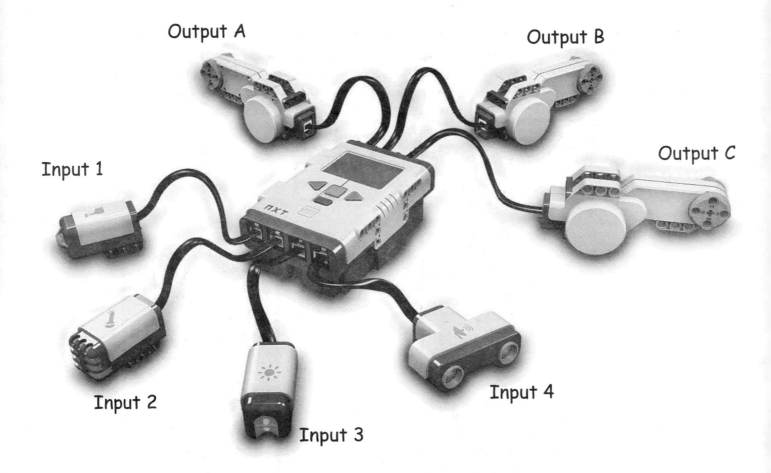

Output A

Output B

Output C

Input 1

Input 2

Input 3

Input 4

Tip: Connect the sensors and motors to the default or "standard" ports, so that programming becomes easier because it starts out using the same ports that you have used for the connections.

Differential
Drive
System

"The plan may be useless but planning is essential." - Eisenhower

The Robot

One of the most important thing for the team to build is the robot.   The most practical and common drive system for robots used in FLL™ competition is the Differential Drive system.

So let's take a look at the Differential Drive system.

The Differential Drive

This drive system means that there are two independent motors, one on each side of the robot.   When both wheels are being turned in the same direction by the motors, the robot moves forwards or backwards. When one wheel is spinning in one direction or both wheels are spinning in opposite directions, the robot turns right or left.   The front wheels are "skid" wheels, which means they simply slip and slide across whatever surface the robot moves upon and in fact should have little to no traction on that surface.   To that end, I prefer skids that roll, i.e., the hubs of wheels without the tires instead of pieces that slide, because there is less friction.

Advantages

Simple to build and implement and probably the most commonly used drive system.
Strong robot, as two motors are employed in moving the robot. This means the manipulator or deliverable items can be larger or heavier.

Disadvantages

Will NOT go in a straight line unless motors are matched and there is no irregular friction on either side.
All motors have some slight variation from their specifications so it is wise to spend time to find two motors that have roughly the same speed (expressed in RPM) and use those for the robot drive system.

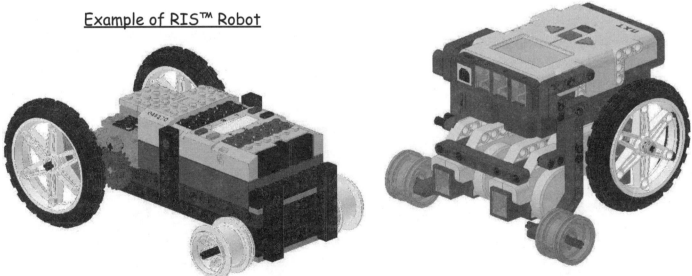

Example of NXT™ Robot

Example of RIS™ Robot

There are alternatives to moving a robot and some are better suited than others for a specific purpose. These six other drive systems may be more complex and not as practical for robotics at this level, but they are discussed in the Appendix.

Building
a
Basic
Competition
Robot

"How do you get to Carnegie Hall? Practice, practice, practice.
How do you evaluate a solution? Observe, observe, observe."
- K.K. Quah

Background

When I am at FLL™ tournaments, especially when I am a judge, I often see rookie teams coming in with the Tri-bot as their robot platform. The typical reason is that most novice teams do NOT have a lot of experience in robot building (as that takes a lot more familiarity and experience with the subject matter) and so using the basic NXT™ Tri-bot found in the retail set seems like a good idea. A lot of teams never seem to ask if Tri-bot is a good "competition robot." On the one hand, it is easy to build and they are familiar with Tri-bot because they probably worked with it and experimented with it. Navigation seems to be easy with Tri-bot and it uses a differential drive system. The skid wheel in Tribot is a caster wheel and that is where the issues start.

Here is an experiment you can try. The next time you are in a supermarket, get a shopping cart and, after loading it move it, forward for, say four feet then suddenly pull it backwards by the handle and see if it will move backward exactly a straight line. As you will observe, the cart will likely not reverse directions in a straight line a lot of the time. This is a problem with caster wheels.

In the typical example of Tri-bot which has the differential drive system and the caster wheels, when it moves forward and then is moved backward, the swiveling action of the caster wheels makes an unintended motion which can make the wheels diverge. You can run this experiment with your Tri-bot. Program it to go four feet, then reverse directions to see if it will return to the same spot. This is one of my acid tests for building a good robot. To make it even harder, program the robot to run almost the length of an FLL™ table, say close to eight feet, then reverse to see how close it comes back to the same launch point.

You can make Tribot work better by just NOT using the caster wheels but instead making the front into fixed skid wheels.

So why am I harping on robots going in a straight line? Two reasons. One is that a robot that can reasonably go forward and backward in a straight line will be more predictable and so will have a better chance to complete missions reliably. Second, I have a rule of thumb that goes "About half the FLL™ missions every year can be solved by a program that simply goes forward and backward." In fact, in FLL™ 2005 Ocean Odyssey, I remember my team using the same forward and backward program but with three different manipulators to solve three different missions. This also had the added benefit of taking up less memory for programs so that it simplified which programs were needed.

That is why I am surprised at tournaments when teams do NOT get at least half the mission scores. Certainly, when combining missions, the paths do get more elaborate, but again I ask my team members to look for the simplest and most "straight forward" path available.

Tip: About half the FLL™ missions can be solved with a robot going forward and backward.

Desirable Robot Features

Spend your time accordingly in building a robot platform. Some teams are formed in the Fall. I usually do not recommend going past October in developing and coming up with a design for a robot. I prefer to start on robot design and building very early, even before the season starts. The rationale is that we already know the basic features of the robot that can be used in FLL™ competitions.

Start with a list of features and develop to that list. An example list is given below. You might want to think about what is important to your team in a robot feature. Some features I deem to be required, like having many locations to attach manipulators on the robot, which gives more opportunities in solving missions. Other features might just be desirable but may not even be part of the robot at the end of the build. For example, it might be nice to have a narrow robot which can more easily navigate between mission models, but maybe a final design which is wider gives more stability.

List of Features (R = required, D = desirable)
Differential drive system (D)
Possible sensor attached to front (D)
Small robot dimensions (D) - which will affect the spaces it can squeeze through
Low height of the robot (D) - which may affect the center of gravity
Fast robot (D) - tied to gear ratio and the ability to pull heavier payloads
Many attachment points on the robot (R) - which determines where manipulators can be located. For flexibility, it makes sense to provide as many manipulator attachment points as possible
Light weight robot (D) - which allows for heavier payload
Well balanced robot (R) - center of gravity of the robot correctly situated

Then narrow the robot down to two designs that you are comfortable with and wait for the competition parameters to be announced. Typically, the best builders can come up with a strong design for the robot, so I usually assign this task to my veteran team members who have the most experience and have seen the most designs used in previous competitions. You should know that this kind of robot design experience only comes with more time spent, so if you do not feel you have a good design the first year, evolve it into a better design the next year.

In the following pages, I will have instructions for BasicBot, which I believe to be a good starting point for a competition FLL™ robot. It does use a differential drive system and uses wheels without tires for skids in front. It can be built with set 9797 and set 9648, as mentioned in the list of materials. The robot uses few pieces and is compact.

This is a robot I have used in summer camps to help train my team. My team's current robot has been derived from this base model and is now more elaborate than this, but the basic principles of good design and building are still there.

Tip: Build your robot(s) in Summer or early Fall before the FLL™ season starts.

Instructions for BasicBot

 Dark gray Technic™ Axle Joiner
Perpendicular with 2 holes (2x)

Black long pins (4x)

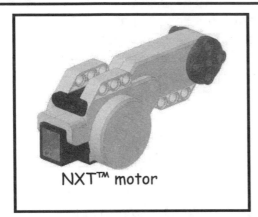

NXT™ motor

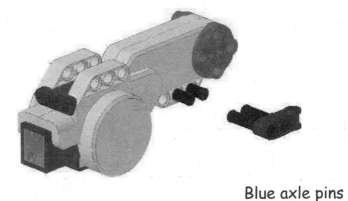

Dark gray Technic™ Axle Joiner
 Perpendicular with 2 holes
Dark gray Technic™ Beam 9
Blue axle pins (4x)

Blue axle pins

Dark gray Technic™ Axle Joiner
 Perpendicular with 2 holes
NXT™ motor
Axle 6 (2x)
Bushings (2x)
Yellow Half bushings (2x)
Black pins (4x)

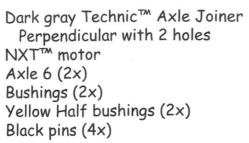

Copyright © 2008 Technology Learning Classes for Kids

Dark grayTechnic™ beam 9
Dark gray liftarm 3x5 L shape (2x)
Black pins (4x)

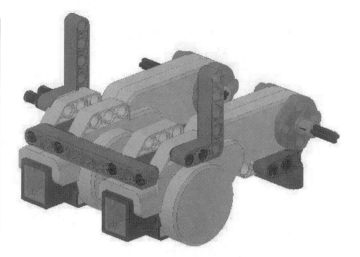

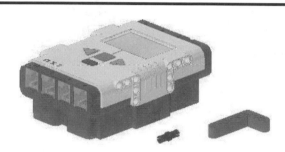

NXT™ Intelligent Brick
Black pins (8x)
Dark gray liftarm 3x5 L shape (2x)

Blue axle pins (2x)
Black pins (6x)

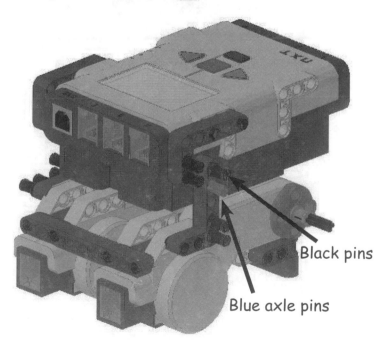

Black pins

Blue axle pins

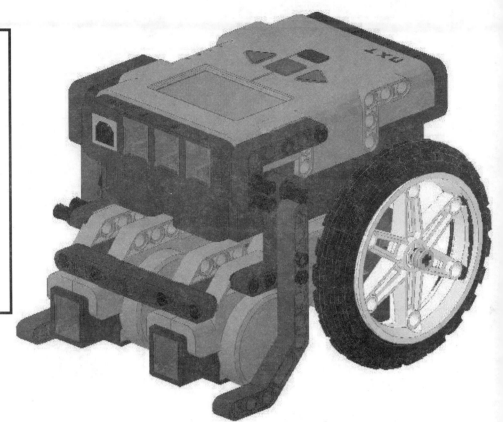

Dark gray Liftarm 1x11.5
 double bent (2x)
Tire 81.6x15 motorcycle (2x)
Wheel 81.6x15 motorcycle
(2x)
Yellow Half Bushing (2x)

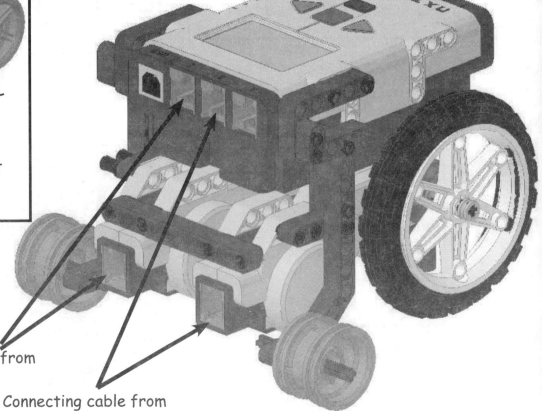

Dark gray liftarm 2x4 L
 shape (2x)
Dark gray axle 5.5
 with stops (2x)
Wheel 43.2x22 without
pinholes, with external
ribs (2x)

Connecting cable from
port C to motor

Connecting cable from
port B to motor

Introduction
to
Programming
Using
NXT-G™

"Nothing is a waste of time if you use the experience wisely."
- Auguste Rodin

Introduction to Programming BasicBot

The NXT™ set comes with a disk which has a graphical programming language called NXT-G™. It really is a wonderful way to introduce robotics as it is very easily learned and is also capable of doing some complex programs.

A program is a set of instructions to tell the robot what to do. The NXT-G™ allows you to write the instructions in an icon-based graphical way and then transfer the program onto the robot. You can do this either through the USB wire or, if you can get the robot's Bluetooth to talk to your PC or laptop, you can wirelessly transfer or download the program.

Let's get started.

First build BasicBot. This robot has a differential drive because it uses one motor on each side connected to a wheel. The front wheels are not powered by motors and will skid or roll freely if the robot is moved about. The differential drive robot is the most basic kind of robot to build and the easiest to navigate, so we will start with it.

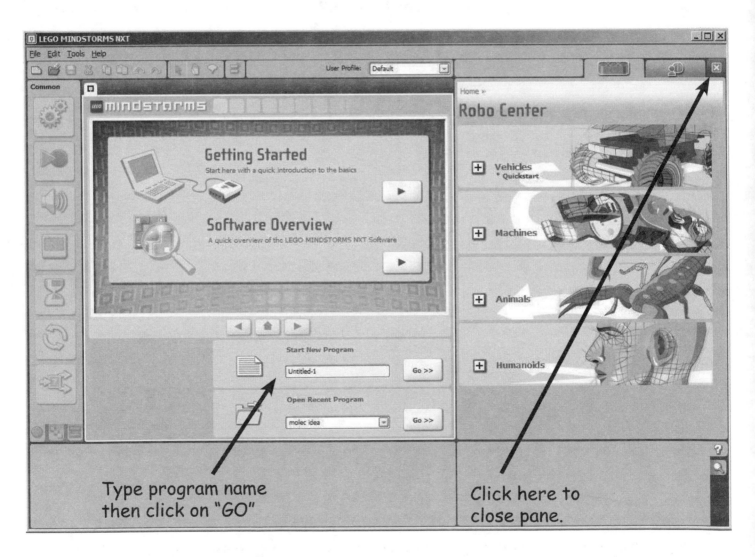

Type program name
then click on "GO"

Click here to
close pane.

When you double click on the NXT™ programming icon, you will see the screen above. I usually close out the right pane by clicking on the "x" on the right-hand side. Then type in "Test1", then click on Go.

Copyright © 2008 Technology Learning Classes for Kids

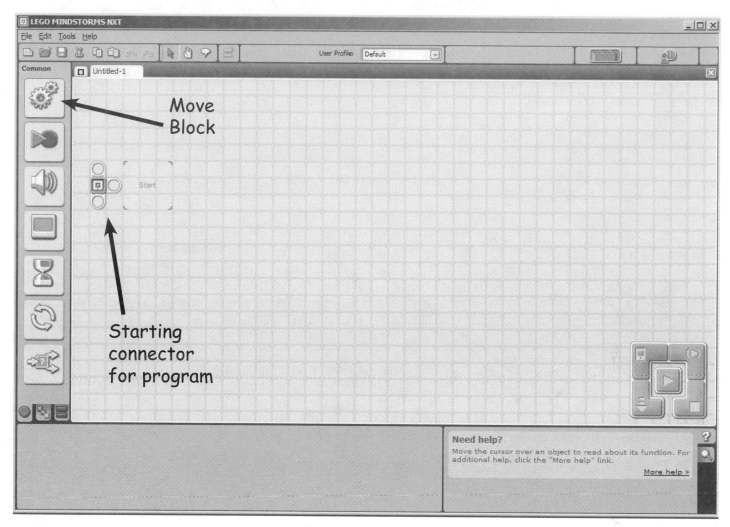

You will now see the programming screen above.   Note that the blocks on the left side are for you to drag onto the starting connector.   When you do this you start a program.

The left panel blocks are named as follows:

MOVE block - As the name implies, it allows a movement, involving the motor(s) to happen

RECORD/PLAY block - for recording and playing back

SOUND block - for use with the sound sensor

DISPLAY block - for showing values on the LCD display

WAIT block - for inserting pauses (waits)

LOOP block - for inserting repeatable tasks (loops)

SWITCH block - for inserting conditional tasks (switching between two branches of commands)

Drag one MOVE Block from the left panel onto the right of the starting connector.   Look at all the settings at the bottom section. You may have to set the ports, direction, steering, power, duration and next action.

Navigation Exercise 1 - Forward/Backward Motion

Now duplicate the program on the next page by dragging a MOVE Block onto the working area. Also, duplicate all the settings for the ports (most of which should be correct if you use the default settings), direction (forward), steering (center), power (set at 75). Change the duration to one rotation and leave the next action as Brake.

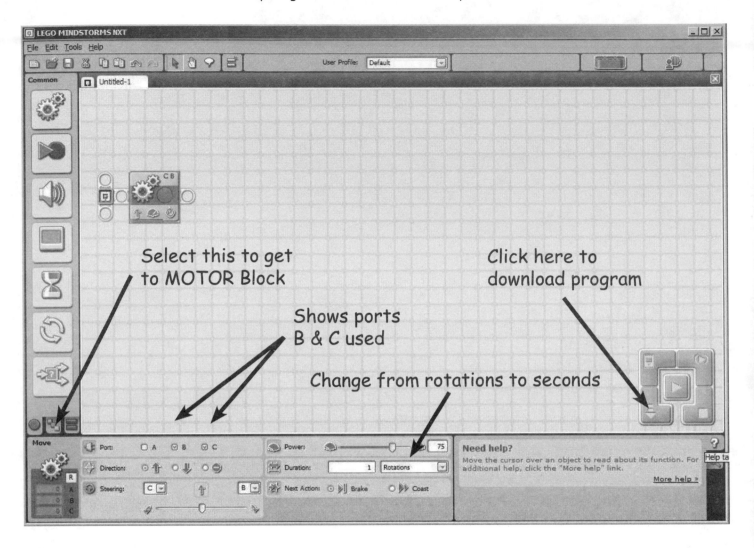

Connect the USB cable from the laptop/PC to the robot.   Then click the button indicated above to download the program.   You will see a dialog box running which will tell you when the program is compiled and downloaded.

Use the orange button on the NXT™ Intelligent Brick to get to the program Test1. You can get to it following the sequence pictured on the right. Run Test1 by pressing the orange button again. What happens to the robot?

It should go forward for one second, then stop. Congratulations ! You have just written your first NXT-G™ program.

Now change the program to make the robot move forward five seconds and then backward five seconds.   Run it to test the program. Do NOT forget to download the program after you have changed it.

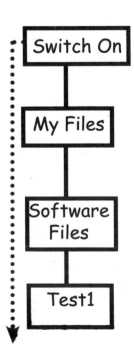

Summary of Basic Forward and Backward Motion

To go forward, both motors have to turn at the same time, at the same rate, and for the same duration in the forward direction.

To go backward, both motors have to turn at the same time, at the same rate, and for the same duration in the backward direction.

MOTOR and MOVE Blocks

We have seen the MOVE Block which allows for motion in the motor.   For every kind of motion in the robot, you have to make some decisions about how it is moved. There is another command called the MOTOR Block which is found in the complete palette section. To get to this you go to the bottom of the left panel and click on the middle tab.

The **MOTOR Block** switches the motors on and off but does not have any control mechanism to slow down the motor as it gets to the duration you have set. So if you have set the motor to go for one rotation, it may get past one rotation before stopping.

Also, the motor block has an Action Panel which allows for the following settings - constant, ramp up and ramp down.   The constant setting basically means the motor will move at a constant rate upon activation.   The ramp up means the motor will start from zero and slowly get to the power level you have set the motor to run, kind of like accelerating in a car.   The ramp down then means the opposite of ramp up, which is that the motor will slow down from an initial speed before stopping. However, in order for the ramp down to work, you need to precede the MOTOR Block with the ramp down setting with a MOTOR Block with a constant setting in order to give the motor an initial speed to ramp down from.

The **MOVE Block**, on the other hand, does have some control mechanism which will slow the motor down as it gets to the duration you have set, so that it will likely get just one rotation and no more.

So when should you use a MOTOR Block and when should you use a MOVE Block?

It truly depends on your intentions and objectives. In most cases for maximum control you would typically use the MOVE Block.   Using the MOVE Block for motion in a robot will mean that the robot will not overshoot its set duration; e.g. it will only go one rotation and no more.

However, in some cases I have found the MOTOR Block to be useful, especially when you want the robot to turn and deliberately contact some object - a deliberate overshoot.   This is useful in motion to a target as it will mean the motion will have more "authority" to it and contact to the target is firm.

Navigation Exercise 2 - Turns

There are two kinds of turns that you can make the robot do.

One is a simple turn which uses only one of the wheels while the other wheel is stopped, as shown on right. Once again, you can use either the MOVE Block for more control or the MOTOR Block for some overshooting.

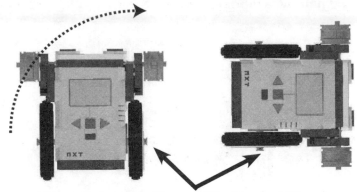

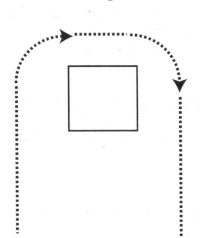

Pivot Point for Turn with Single Wheel

Turns Using One Motor Only.

Write a program to do roughly the following U-shaped path around a simple obstacle.

How many MOVE Blocks did you need to make this work?

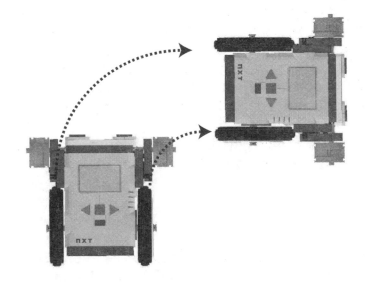

There are many ways to write this program, but you might need about five MOVE Blocks - one to go forward from a starting position, one to make the turn, one to go forward to get past the obstacle, one to make another right-hand turn, and finally one to make the forward motion back to the starting area.
This seems as if it uses a lot of blocks, but it will give you a more precise turn.

Turns Using Both Motors

The MOVE Block has a slider bar on the left side.   If you shift the slider bar, from one side to the other, it will control both motors, but it will either spin, make a arc, pivot about a point and, if you leave it in the middle, go in a straight line.

However, the exact position on the slider bar to control this may need some trial and error.

The most likely use of this is to make an arcing motion where the wheel on one side moves forward faster than the wheel on the other side.

Using the slider bar then makes turns a little less predictable in terms of precise control over the turn. In fact, I recommend using one motor to control turns if you want to be more precise.

Write a program to make the robot do the following turn around an obstacle. Note that the path here can be a little different than the previous U-shaped path.

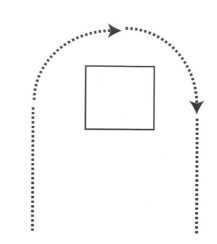

How many MOVE blocks did you need to make this work?

Again, there are many solutions, but if you use the slider bar to move both motors in a gentle arc, you might be able to work this path in just three or four MOVE Blocks.

Try running the same program five times in a row. Does the robot always follow exactly the same path? <u>Answer: It may have slight variations because of friction in the tires.</u>

Again the choice of the MOVE block or the MOTOR block for the turn depends on the objective you desire.

Useful Geometry Review

In this next section, let's review some useful geometry and other mathematics concepts which will help make for better robot navigation.

Rotations and Degrees in Navigation

We first should review circles and their properties, as the wheel is simply a circle in shape.

We must be able to identify the following:

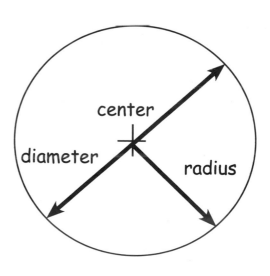

The <u>center</u> of a circle, which in a wheel is the point where the axle is usually located.

The <u>radius</u> is the distance from the center to the rim.

The <u>diameter</u> is the distance from the rim through the center to the other edge of the rim.

The <u>circumference</u> is the distance along the rim of the circle all around the circle.

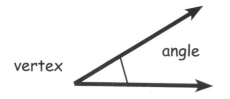

Angles

The other useful piece of information is a review of angles and the mathematics associated with angles. Two rays that have the same endpoint form an angle. The endpoint is called the vertex. Angles are measured in degrees.

Basic Angles

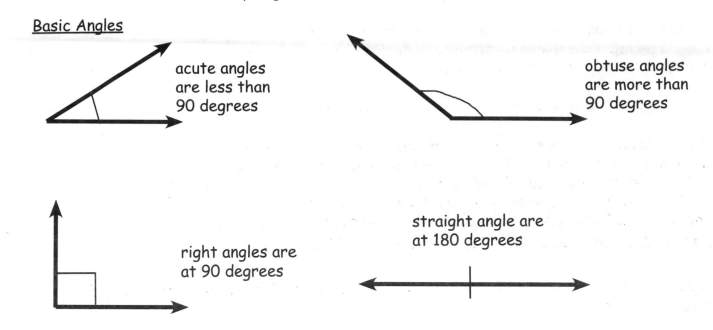

Math with Angles

Also, note that one full circumference is one rotation of a circle.
Half a rotation is a straight angle of 180 degrees.
One full rotation is 360 degrees.
Two full rotations is 360 x 2 = 720 degrees.
One and a half rotations is 360 + 180 = 540 degrees.

Since the NXT™ motors are accurate to one degree, this means that for the most precise measurement, you should use degrees for programming movement, as it is far more accurate to go 413 degrees than 413/360 = 1.427222...rotations.

One important thing is to know the distance travelled by your robot.   To do this we must apply the formula for the circumference of a circle.

Circumference of a circle   = 2 x pi x Radius OR
                                              = pi x Diameter(D)

The easiest formula to use is pi x D. Since we can estimate pi to be 3.14, all we need to do is find the diameter of the wheels that are being powered by the motor. In BasicBot, that refers to the diameter of the wheel in the back of the robot.   We can directly measure the wheel by simply taking it off the robot and using a ruler.

One we have that, we can apply the formula:

Distance travelled in one rotation = 3.14 x Diameter of wheel.

Once we have this information, we can use it in one of two ways. One is to use a tape measure to measure the distance the robot needs to travel to a target, then divide this by the distance traveled in one rotation, which will give us the number of rotations we need to use in the program to get to that distance.

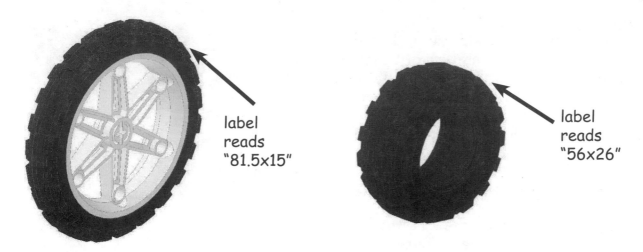

label reads "81.5x15"

label reads "56x26"

The measurements for the wheels are conveniently found on the tires, but stated in metric in millimeters.   So in the above examples, the 81.5 means the wheel diameter is 81.5 mm.

We then use the formula to calculate circumference, which is the distance traveled in one rotation:

Circumference   = pi x diameter of wheel
                       = 3.14 x 81.5 mm
                       = 256 mm or 25.6 cm
                       = 256 x 0.03937 inches
                       = 10.08 inches or roughly 10 inches.

So if we need the robot to go two feet or 24 inches, the number of rotations we need to put on the MOVE Block is 24/10 or 2.4 rotations.

Use of View in Navigation

One other method is to use the View capabilities.   From the Menu Tree pictured at right, we get there by first switching on the IB, using the arrows right/left till we get to View, then selecting View; use the right arrow button until you get to Motor degrees, then select Motor degrees.

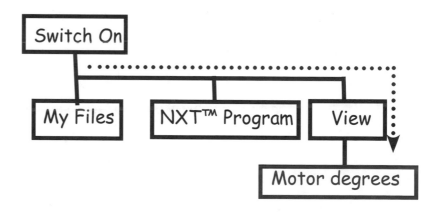

Then place the robot at the base where you would start the robot, then firmly drag the robot to the target location taking care not to let the wheels slip off the table. When you look at the LCD panel it will give you the distance traveled by the wheels in degrees, which you can then plug into the MOVE Block to get an initial distance before you make any adjustments.

You could of course do this for Motor rotations as well.   However, the distance in degrees will be more accurate and precise.

Get the team to try this out on a field or just on any table surface. Ask them to drag a robot exactly 20 inches and see if that corresponds to two rotations or 720 degrees of the wheel motion of BasicBot.

The Geometry of Turns

One typical action you would like to do is make the robot make a right-hand or left-hand turn of 90 degrees. However, you should know that this is just an orientation but likely not the number of degrees that the robot wheels will need to spin. In other words, making the robot wheel turn 90 degrees will likely not result in a perfect right or left-hand turn.

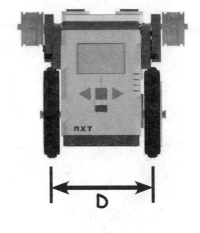

Why? Because a turn depends on both the circumference of the robot and the distance between the wheels.

If you pivot a robot about the left wheel, as in the figure on the right, it makes a half-circle to turn all the way around, or the equivalent of two 90-degree left turns.

The radius of the circle inscribed is the distance between the wheels, which can be measured or computed using the geometry of the pieces.

Distance (D) between wheels or Radius of circle
= 95 mm (measured)

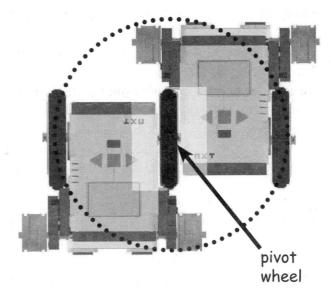

pivot wheel

So half the circumference of the circle
= 0.5 x pi x diameter
= 0.5 x pi x (2 x 95)
= 298.3 mm

Half again this to get the distance the wheel needs to move in a quarter circle
= 298.3 x 0.5
= 149.15 mm

This distance needs to be converted back to a form we can use, i.e. rotations.

Rotations for exact 90 degree turn   = Distance traveled in quarter turn/circumference wheel
                                        = 149.15/256
                                        = 0.58 rotations
                                        = 0.58 x 360 degrees
                                        = 210 degrees

So if we need the robot to make a 90-degree left or right turn, we need to move the right or left wheel 210 degrees or 0.58 rotations.

Seems like a lot of calculations to go through, but this is a more precise way to define the navigation of the robot. Most team members usually just estimate the turn and make adjustments until they get what they like.

However, having this calculation can help you check your work as well.

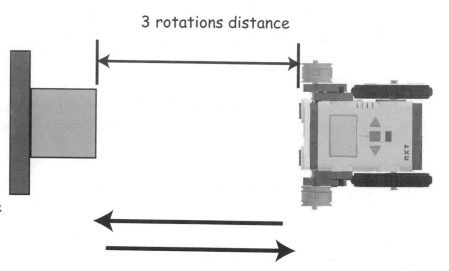

3 rotations distance

Use of Rotations vs. Timer (Seconds)

One common question I get from new coaches is whether, in programming movement, the team should use rotations or seconds. Let's look at some detailed cases.

Here we have the robot at an exact distance of three rotations to a target that is braced against the side of a wall of the mission table.

Case 1

We program a MOVE block of 2.8 rotations; the robot stops just shy of the target and is able to achieve its objective. The robot then reverses direction to the start.

Case 2

We program a MOVE block of exactly three rotations; the robot contacts the target and is able to achieve its objective. The robot then reverses direction to the start.

Case 3

We program a MOVE block of 3.2 rotations and the robot bumps into the target and stops. The wheels are locked and the robot is NOT able to move, as the program says, to another 0.2 rotations, but the wheels are unable to do so and the rotation sensor built into the motors is reading that the program is still not complete. Because the robot did not complete the last program instruction, i.e., 0.2 more rotations, the robot is stuck and will not reverse back to the start. You will have to manually handle the robot. Some surfaces may be slick enough that the robot wheels slip the last 0.2 rotations, then the robot reverses, but you cannot count on this for the mission table surface.

The conclusion is that if we overshoot a target using rotations for movement, we may end up with a robot that is stuck in contact with the target.

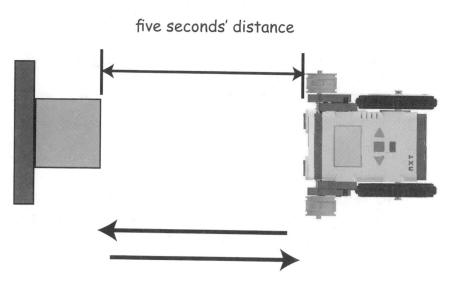

five seconds' distance

Here we have the robot at an exact distance of five seconds to a target that is braced against the side of a wall of the mission table.

Let's run through a few cases for this.

Case 1
We program a MOVE block of 4.5 seconds and the robot stops just shy of the target and is able to achieve its objective. The robot then reverses direction to the start.

Case 2
We program a MOVE block of exactly five seconds and the robot contacts the target and is able to achieve its objective. The robot then reverses direction to the start.

Case 3
We program a MOVE block of 5.5 seconds and the robot bumps into the target and stops for 0.5 seconds more, then reverses direction to the start.

In this scenario, the robot does not get stuck and does reverse back to the start. So this seems better that the rotation sensor. There is one hitch.

Timing is dependent on the state of the batteries. So if the robot is always fully charged, it will likely perform as programmed, but if the batteries are low, what used to take five seconds exactly might now take six seconds, There is a possibility that the robot might not be able to achieve the objectives.

So we are still left with the question, what should we use?

Again it depends on the objective. Sometimes, using rotations is fine. The example that comes to mind is the FLL™ mission in Ocean Odyssey to tag the gray fish without touching the green fish. The fish are out in the open and loose. So a carefully measured number of rotations would bump the gray fish, but only slightly so that it does not touch any of the green fish. And since, the robot will not get stuck in contact with the target, this works great.

However, one recommendation is to use a combination of both settings. There is no reason not to use two MOVE blocks to accomplish the objectives.

1 second   2.8 rotations distance

Here we have the robot with two MOVE blocks. One moves the robot 2.8 rotations to target. The second one moves it the remaining one second deliberately overshooting and contacting the target. This way, we know we can achieve the objective and make contact with the target but we reduce the time of the contact.

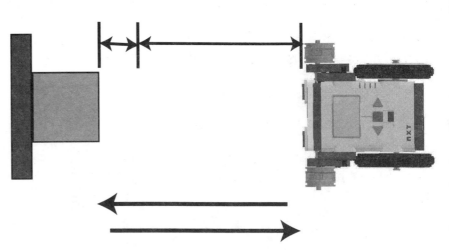

The conclusion here is that we can combine the best of both the rotation setting and the timer setting to achieve the objective with minimal problems.

So by the end of this day, we should have a good grasp of robot navigation.

Introduction
to
Manipulators
and
Challenges

"The greatest challenge to any thinker is stating the problem in a way that will allow a solution." - Bertrand Russell

Day 2
Notes on Challenges
After some lessons, we will be working on challenges, which are just problems to give you a chance to apply your creativity in solving a problem. Note that the lesson always contains valuable information to help you with your challenge.
The challenge almost always involve using a robot and modifying it to your needs. You will also likely need to build some manipulators which will help you in the challenge. And you need to understand the restrictions or engineering constraints if any are stated.

The Three Ps of a Challenge
Challenges involve working out the following - Path, Program and Pieces.

Path - this is the path your robot will need to take in order to reach the target area and complete the challenge. Planning the path is a good thing to do. Note that in some challenges you will need to get the robot to target and return it to base. In other challenges, you can complete the challenge as a one-way trip and NOT have to return to base.

Program - this is what you will need to write to make the robot navigate along the path. The path will determine the program.

Pieces - these are what you will need to use to modify the robot OR in most cases just add a manipulator to the robot to solve the mission. Again, planning the path helps determine the kind of pieces you need to solve the mission, because the destination of the path on the side of the target may affect the pieces needed.

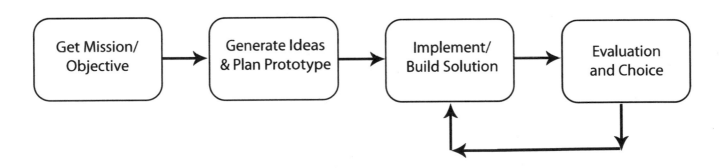

Typical Problem Solving Process in FLL™
The typical things to do in solving problems are:
1. Obtain mission/objective/problem/challenge
2. Generate ideas and plan solution (consider the three Ps)
3. Build prototype
4. Test solution. Observe and evaluate solution
5. Improve solution
6. Repeat steps 4 to 6 until best solution is found

Observation is very important. You cannot improve a solution unless you see what is wrong with the solution or what needs to be added/changed to make it work better. Make observations over many trials, NOT just a single trial.

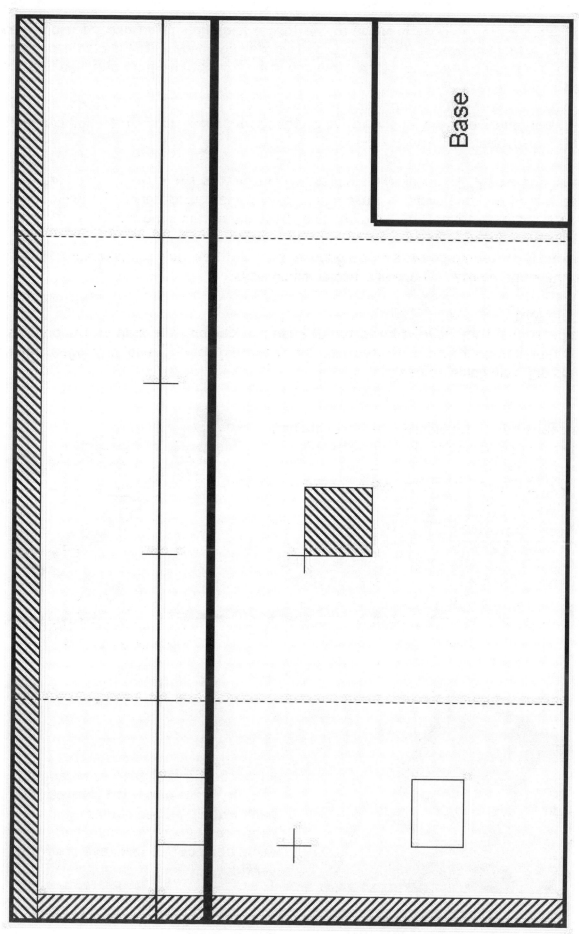

Path Planning Sheet for Missions

Base

Path

The path of the robot from the base location to the target is an important one. I usually let the team work from a planning sheet like the one on the previous page. This is also important so that during "down" time not at the table, the team can still stare at the field and come up with alternate paths to the target.

Every year someone usually comes up with a mock-up of the year's FLL™ challenge that fits on an 8.5" x 11" sheet, and I am very appreciative of those who come up with it. You can likely find it on the FLL™ question and answer forums.

So, what makes a good path? As usual, the simplest and easiest is the straight line forward from base to the target and backward to base again. Sometimes turns cannot be avoided, but if there is a way to make it to target in a straight line, I usually recommend that.

Starting from exactly the same point is also a good thing. But how do you make sure that the robot starts at the same point? There are two common ways.

Marks on the Field Mat

In FLL™ competitions, they have started to put hash marks along the side of the base as landmarks to aid teams in getting a consistent, specific starting point. Also, any logos, brands or other markings are fair game to use.

Jigs

Sometimes, the robot has to be oriented at an angle and it's hard to ensure the right angle. To help with this, teams are allowed to use jigs.

A jig is simply a tool made out of pieces to help a robot align to a specific side wall or edge of the mat. They do not have to be complex but they should at least be rigid and maintain the position of launch. These jigs can vary from very small to very large. The use of jigs is recommended even if some team members can seem to launch a robot fairly consistently from base. The idea is that, with a jig, anyone on the team can run the mission.

Parts List for Jig
Technic Beam 1x16 (2x)
Technic Beam 1x8
Plate 1x6
Plate 1x4 (5x)
Plate 1x3 (2x)

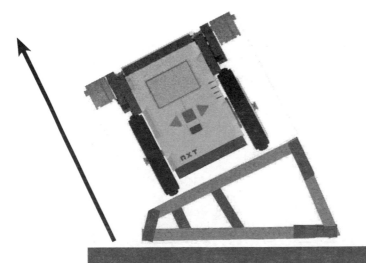

Here the jig is aligned to an edge of a field mat and, with the robot's back wheels placed against it, the robot can reliably be launched at an angle of about 29 degrees from the vertical.

Program

Once the path of the robot is determined, the program should then be derived from the path. This is simply dragging the MOVE or MOTOR blocks onto the starting area and creating the program.   You should always pay close attention to the settings.

Some settings, like the duration (number of degrees), may need to be fine tuned. Also, the speed or power of the robot as it moves to the target may need to be adjusted. Some decisions need to be made depending on the kind of contact you desire with the target. If you need to hit the target, you might deliberately want to overshoot and use the MOTOR block. Or you might want a sustained hit so you have two MOVE blocks, one getting the robot close to the target using rotations, then using a MOVE block with seconds to get it to sustain a hit on the target.

All these decisions need to be made as you write your program.

Pieces (Manipulators)

The pieces are the manipulators, which are the tools you can attach to the robot to help you complete the mission. Manipulators have to fit the purpose of the mission.

Shaped Manipulators

As the name implies, this type of manipulator is designed so that its shape is more effectively used to complete the mission.   It is best used in delivery missions to move some desired token to the target area. The shape must be considered carefully so that the delivered item is trapped in the manipulator but will be released when the robot leaves the target.

This manipulator is also suitable for a mission that simply requires the robot to trigger or hit the target.

Any number of shapes can be considered, for example a U shape, a V shape, a T-bar shape, etc. Even a simple stick can be the appropriate shape given the right mission.

Example - Shaped Manipulator

Here is a simple shaped manipulator that can be used in front of the robot to move a gear token from behind a line to touch a second line.   The gear token would fit nicely between the black long friction pins.

Step 1
Black pin (2x)
Black axle joiner perpendicular
   1x3x3 with 4 pins (2x)
Black Technic™ pin joiner round(2x)

Step 2
Gray liftarm 2x4 L shaped (2x)
Black pin long (4x)
Black pin (2x)
Dark gray liftarm 1x5 straight
Axle 3 with stud (2x)

Token fits here

Robot Modifications - Wall Guides

Now that you have some familiarity with BasicBot, it's time to try a few things to improve it. Keep in mind, the more predictable you can make the robot move to target, the more effective your robot will be in the mission.

Let's first add a wall guide, which will help BasicBot move along a wall easily.

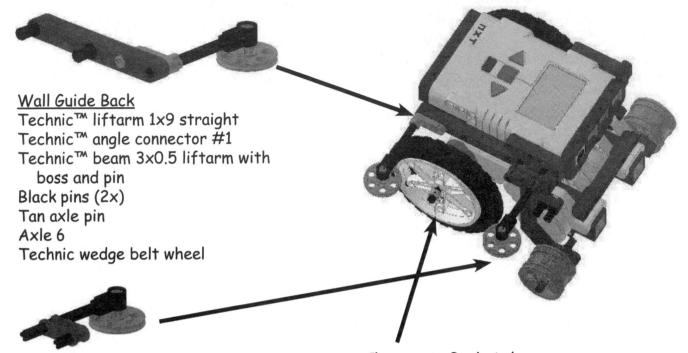

Wall Guide Back
Technic™ liftarm 1x9 straight
Technic™ angle connector #1
Technic™ beam 3x0.5 liftarm with
    boss and pin
Black pins (2x)
Tan axle pin
Axle 6
Technic wedge belt wheel

Wall Guide Front
Technic™ axle joiner perpendicular 3L
Technic™ angle connector #1
Tan axle pin
Axle 6
Axle 2
Technic™ wedge belt wheel

Changes to Back Axle
The wheels needed to be moved to make room for the wheel guides. The axle 6 was changed to axle 8. An extra bushing was added so that both large motorcycle wheels are moved further apart.

As a result of this modification, the robot now has wall guides, which allow the robot to move along a wall and follow the contours of the wall at an exact distance even if it started at an angle to the wall but is traveling toward it.

This will allow the robot to get to a target which is a set a little off from a wall.

Can you think of other wheels that can be used to make the wall guide work better?

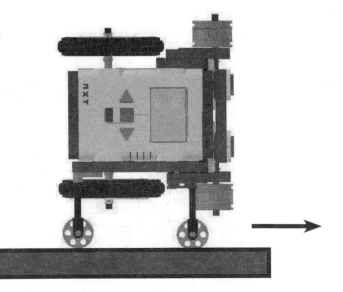

Robot Modifications - Front Panel or Grill

Here's another very useful thing to modify on BasicBot - a front panel which gives you more areas to attach manipulators.   The important thing here is to make sure the "grill" will not fall apart and is firmly anchored to the front of BasicBot, but you are still able to take it off to access both the input ports and the USB port to download programs.

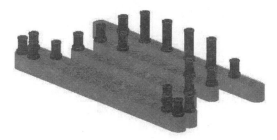

Front Panel - Step 1
Liftarm 1x15 straight (3x)
Beam 11 (2x)
Black pins (16x)
Black pins long (4x)

Front Panel - Step 2
Beam 13
Beam 7 (2x)
Hassen pins (4x)
Axle joiner perpendicular double split (2x)

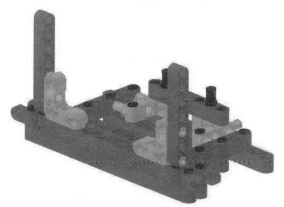

Front Panel - Step 3
Beam 7 (2x)
Black pins (2x)

Black pins long with stop bushing (4x)

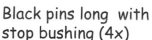

As a result of this modification, the robot now has a very large front panel (grill) on which many manipulators can be attached. There are also some more attachment areas on the sides. This is to help make the solutions more flexible, as more kinds of manipulators can be put on the robot for use in missions.

Can you think of other modifications that can make the robot better?

Challenges

Most of the camp time will involve challenges, which are basically missions that are given to the students to try out on a more simplified field mat that can be created using very inexpensive materials. The details of the mission mat and setup are in the Appendix and you should create all of these items ahead of time.

You should also cover the following general rules.

General Rules for All Missions

All robots MUST start at base.

Base is defined as the 10 inch x 10 inch square on the bottom right-hand side of the field mat. Note that the robot must have all wheels/skids start on base, but manipulators can stick out over the field and cross the base border. This is different from FLL™ rules, because this field mat is much smaller, so I feel a relaxation is fine for the purposes of learning and more flexibility. In FLL™, the robot and manipulator must fit inside base.

If a robot leaves base and is stuck out in the field, then the mission trial is over.

A robot that has been programmed to return to base can be handled. A robot operator may grab the robot any time the robot or a manipulator breaks the plane of the base border. The robot operator may then switch to a different program and send the robot out again.

Each team can have a maximum of three mission trials unless otherwise stated.

Each mission trial lasts 30 seconds.

Score is computed at the end of the mission trial and with the state of the field at that time.

There will be specific rules for each of the missions in the following pages.

Mission Management

I allocate about 90 minutes for the missions. You can help each person or team by helping them manage their time properly. For example, if I leave it up to the teams to decide when they have to take each of the three trials, many of them will simply wait until the last minute and try to take all three trials close to the end.

Instead I recommend the following time breakout for each of the missions.

Challenge Rules and Q&A	- 5 minutes
Planning and prototypes	- 45 minutes
Mandatory First Trial	- at the 50th minute
More evaluation and adjustments	- 20 minutes
Mandatory Second Trial	- at the 70th minute (1 hour 10 minutes)
More evaluation and adjustments	- 20 minutes
Final Trial	- at the 90th minute (1.5 hours)

The reason for the mandatory trial is so that the team does NOT wait till the last minute to test. Hands-on testing on the field is essential to learning to solve the challenge properly and also in observing and evaluating the issues to be solved.

You may give some advice by helping them get to the right observations. The score is secondary, but the correct observation to lead to a better solution is essential.

Let's go on to the first challenge!

Token Delivery Challenge

Build a robot to deliver two tokens into area #1 and two tokens into area #2 in the time limit of 30 seconds. The tokens need only break the plane of the lines forming the square. The robot cannot touch the gray-colored plate obstacle. If it is touched, then the trial is over.

Note: the robot does NOT have to deliver all tokens in one trip. However, it must return to base if you want to change programs and send it out again.

You can borrow the design plans from previous robot lessons.

Scoring

Each team gets 10 points for a working program that gets the robot close to the target. There will be four tokens and 10 points for each token successfully delivered.

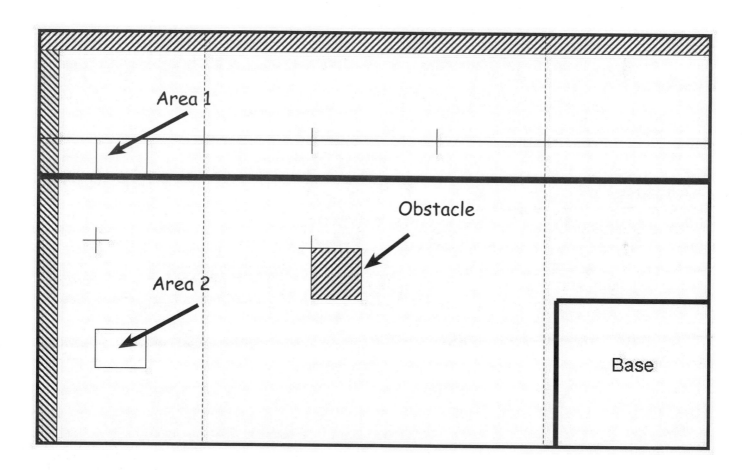

Lessons Learned

You can wrap-up the day with a discussion of the best manipulators or features of manipulators you have seen developed and some observations on how the robots might be improved further.

Day 3

Introduction to the Light Sensor

Here are a few words to help you understand the light sensor.

Threshold – a level, point or value above which something is true and below which something is not true.

Ambient Light – the amount of light at a particular location which can affect sensors.

Average – For two values, it is the middle point between them (value 1 plus value 2 divided by 2).

How the Light Sensor Works

The sensor shoots a beam of light and a receiver detects the amount of reflected light that comes back. The light sensor detects the changes in light and gives the signal to the IB as a percentage between 0 to 100. A very bright light might give a signal of 80, normal room light is around 50 and a dark room might be around 20.

Many things can affect a light sensor, other light sources in the room, batteries in the IB, etc. You should always look at the light values using View to help you decide how to program a robot to work properly.

Light Sensor Exercise 1 - Basic Light Readings

Build BasicBot and attach the light sensor to the front of the robot.   Get to the View ...

Procedure for View

Use the pictured Menu tree to get to Reflected Light, select with the Orange button, press right arrow button twice to get to Port 3, select with Orange button. The light sensor should now come on with the red light, and a value in percentage should be displayed on the IB display.   You are now ready to take a reading.

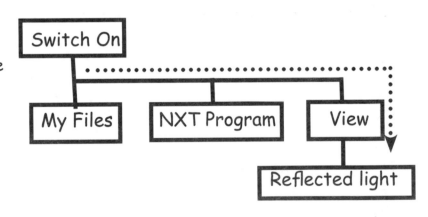

Instructions for Placing Light Sensor

Technic™ Axle Joiner Per-
pendicular 1x3x3 with 4 pins
Hassen pins (2x)
Light Sensor

Reverse Angle View

Final placement of the Light Sensor in the front of the robot with sensor pointing down and centered.
Do not forget the connecting lead from the sensor to default port 3 on the IB.

Light Sensor Exercise 1 - Understanding Basic Light Sensor Values

Using the test lines from the next page, place the sensor on the thickest black line and on any white area and read the values.
Signal from light sensor on white area =
Signal from light sensor on black line =

Average of value from white and black = (_____ + _____) / 2 = _____

This is a good threshold to use for telling the difference between the black and white areas or any two contrasting colors. Why? Because if the value used is too close to one color, it may give a false or confusing signals to the robot. The average value then represents a value equally distant from the value of the white area and the black line.

Now, move the light sensor up by one hole. It will be a little looser as it will only be held to the Hassen pin by the middle hole of the Light sensor. What this does is effectively raise the height of the sensor relative to the ground (flat surface).

Take the light sensor readings again.

Signal from light sensor on white area =
Signal from light sensor on black line =
Did the values change? It should slightly. You can repeat this with the sensor set even higher on the Hassen pin.
What this shows is that the distance of the light sensor to the surface it is reading DOES matter as it depends on the reflected light to the sensor.
Now shine a flashlight (or lamplight) while you are taking a reading on a black line. Did the value of the black line change? It should increase immediately when extra light is on the line.
This shows that sensors are affected by any light in the area of the surface (ambient light).
 The rule of thumb is to get the light sensor as close as possible to the surface you are trying to read without it interfering with the robot movement. Sometimes it may even warrant building a "hood" for the sensor so that any other light source does not interfere with it.

Uses for Loops

Basic LOOP Forever Block

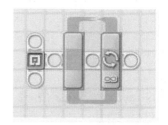

The LOOP Blocks are found on the sixth icon on the left side of the programming interface.   The LOOP Block is used to help reduce programming effort by repeating blocks as needed. It does this by returning to the starting point, usually until some event occurs that satisfies a required condition.

Different Uses of Loops

There are different ways the loop block can be used with the different kinds of control structures or sensors.

	Control	Value Needed
You can loop for x seconds	Timer	Seconds
You can loop for x times	Count	Integer
You can loop until something is True/False	Logic	True/False

OR in the pictures,
you can loop until some sensor value is true. So you can use it with the light sensor to sense light/dark, with the touch sensor when a bump occurs, with the rotation sensor (motor) until some number of rotations is achieved, with the ultrasonic sensor when some distance is achieved or when the sound sensor reaches a certain loudness.

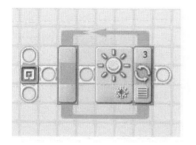 Loop on Light Sensor

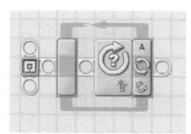 Loop on Rotation Sensor

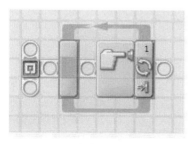 Loop on Touch Sensor

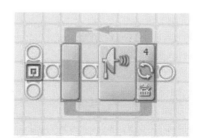 Loop on Ultrasonic Sensor

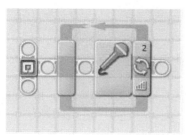 Loop on Sound Sensor

Example

Put a MOVE Block in the middle of a LOOP Block then make the B motor in the MOVE Block run for one second only.

What does this program make the robot do?

Answer: The robot spins continuously.

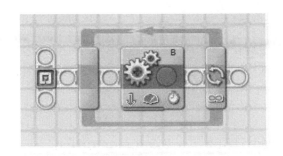

Write the following program, then save it as Test2. The first MOVE Block is an unlimited forward move. The last MOVE Block is a stop block.

What do you think this program makes the robot do?

Answer: The robot will move forward until it encounters a black surface then stops. Note that this program does assume that 50 is the average of a white and black color on a surface.

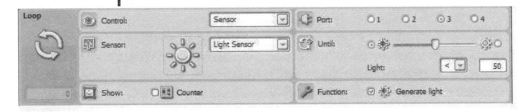

Light Sensor Exercise 2 - Testing with Lines

For this exercise, again using the test lines from the previous page, position BasicBot about eight inches from a line. Then run Test2 program. Run the robot over the four different lines on the test pad given.

At which line does the robot stop? Line [1] [2] [3] [4]

Now move the sensor up one hole higher from the position on the front of the robot.
Test the program again.

At which line does the robot stop? Line [1] [2] [3] [4]

Now use a flashlight on the black lines while the robot is moving towards them.
Test the program again.

At which line does the robot stop? Line [1] [2] [3] [4]

The conclusion is that ambient light (light in the vicinity of the light sensor) can affect the sensor, and also the thickness (or thinness) of the sensed object can affect the ability of the sensor. This should be taken into consideration if you have any plans to use lines or bands on a table for the robot to navigate and use.

One strategy might be to use a black band/line as a stopping point for the robot. Another is to write a more complex program for the robot to follow a black line as a path to the target commonly called a "line following program".

Problems and Fixes for the Light Sensor

Problems	Fixes
The line for detection is too narrow	Select different thicker line
The line for detection is not dark or light enough	Calibrate sensor to ambient light conditions
The robot is too fast and cannot read the line to form a signal	Slow down the robot
The light sensor is too far off the ground. **Rule of thumb**, make it about two plates from the sensor to the ground.	Move sensor closer to ground or make hood for sensor
There are other powerful light sources affecting it.	Calibrate sensor or make hood for sensor

Light Sensor Exercise 3 - Edge Detection

Write a program in which the robot will move forward forever until it encounters a black line. When it encounters the black line, make the robot back off about eight inches, then turn left or right for about 60 degrees. Then repeat this forever. Essentially, you need to write a program that can detect the black edge of an oval shape on the test pad that comes with 9797.

Hint: Start with Test2 program which is used to stop a robot at a line.
Where do you need to add another loop?
What other blocks do you need to add to it to make it work?

Answer: See program blocks below.

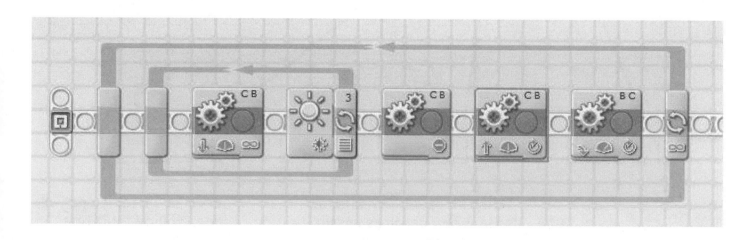

Center of Gravity Based Manipulator

Here are a few useful words to know before we begin discussion on the manipulator.

Center of gravity - the combination of forces of gravity that seems to act at one point in a structure or object

Base - the supporting area of a structure or portion in contact with the ground

When a line drawn straight down from the center of gravity (COG) of an object falls outside the base of that object, it is no longer stable and may fall over. We study COG to help us predict this and can apply this knowledge to manipulators that can fall onto a target to grab it.

Build the COG-based manipulator. Then push it forward fairly quickly and stop suddenly. What happens?

Answer: The long liftarm drops down.

This simple motion works because of a shift in the COG of the long liftarm. When the robot suddenly stops, the long liftarm will swing about the pivot point which is the gray pin and the COG will shift to the front away from the base and fall.

The key is that the COG must be in base but very near the edge of it so that when the robot stops, it will move the COG out of base and fall.

Move up/down to adjust

Step 1
Hassen pin
Liftarm L 3x5
Axle 7, Light gray pin
Technic™ Beam 3x0.5
    Liftarm with Boss &
    Pin (2x)

Step 2
Liftarm 1x15 straight

Mechanics of the COG manipulator

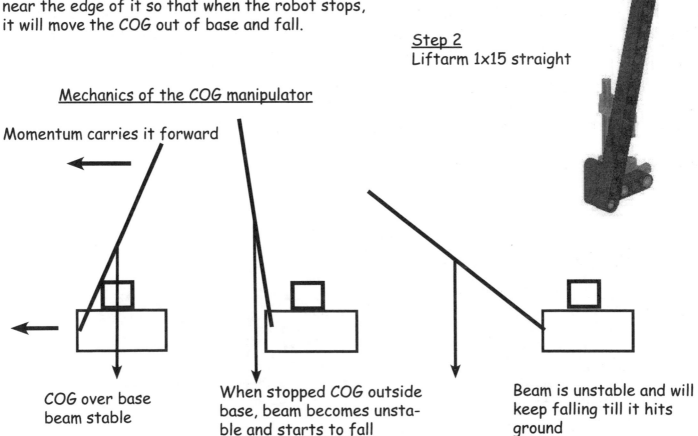

Momentum carries it forward

COG over base
beam stable

When stopped COG outside base, beam becomes unstable and starts to fall

Beam is unstable and will keep falling till it hits ground

COG Manipulator Exercise

Put the COG manipulator you have built on BasicBot.   The long liftarm should be resting on the adjustable piece. Locate the manipulator in the front of BasicBot.

Write a MOVE block to move the robot forward two rotations then stop. Does the long liftarm drop? If it does not drop when the robot stops, how can you make it work?

Keep adjusting the piece on the axle and testing the program until it works.

You also might want to set the power setting lower so that the robot does not prematurely tip the manipulator over. You can also use programming to enhance the solution by introducing a stutter step (a quick backward-and-forward motion to tip the COG manipulator over).

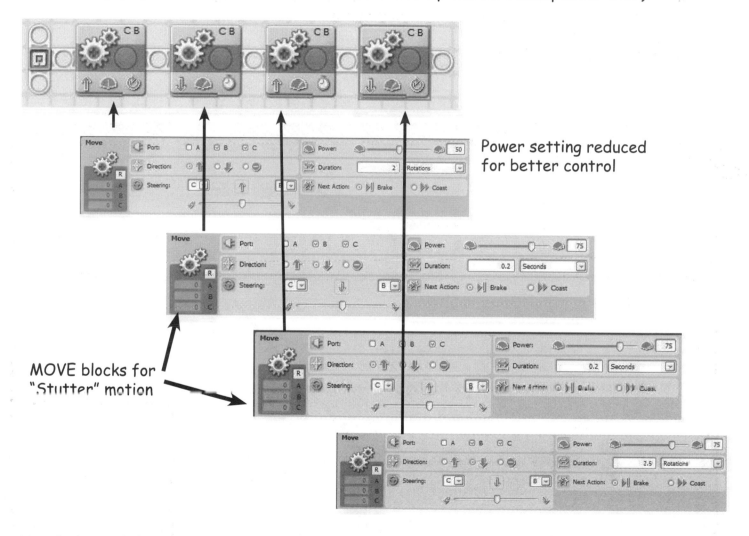

Power setting reduced for better control

MOVE blocks for "Stutter" motion

Now let's send the robot forward and see if it can go forward and grab a gear token located about 20 inches (two rotations) from it and bring it back to a starting point.

Look at the manipulator and ask, what do you need to do to change it so that it can grab a gear token better? Can you add "fingers" to the long liftarm so that when it falls it will grab better? Note: when you add pieces, this will change the COG of the manipulator, so some adjustments to the balance or the program might need to be done.

Multiple Retrieval Challenge

Build a robot to retrieve multiple tokens in the time limit of 30 seconds and bring it back to base. Competition will run for the entire class but each team will get three official tries only. The robot cannot touch the obstacle. If the obstacle is touched, then the trial is over.
Note: the robot does NOT have to retrieve all tokens in one trip. However, it must return to base if you want to change programs and send it out again.

You can borrow design plans from previous robot lessons.

Scoring

Each team gets 10 points for a working program that gets the robot close to the target.
The gear tokens are worth 10 points for each token successfully returned to base.
The triangle token is worth 20 points returned to base.

Set up for the challenge. Place the four tokens in the indicated positions.

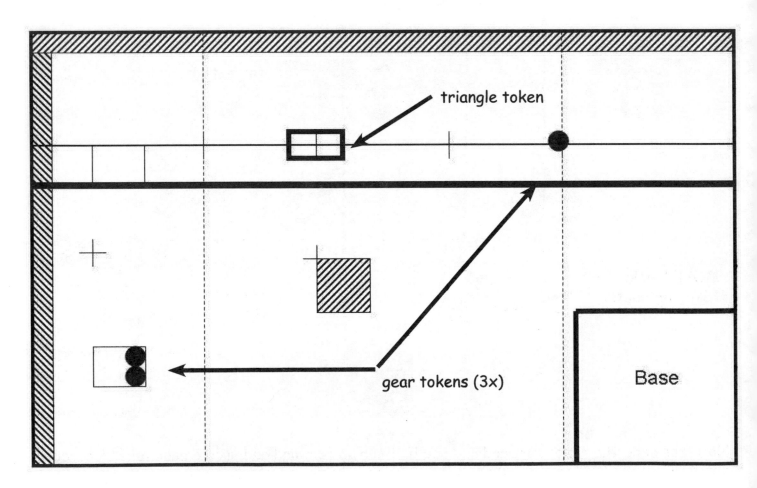

Lessons Learned

You can wrap-up the day with a discussion of the best manipulators or features of manipulators you have seen developed and some observations on how they might be improved even further.

Day 4
Introduction to Ultrasonic Sensor
Here are a few useful words to know before we begin discussion on the ultrasonic sensor.
Ultrasonic – a sound frequency that is beyond the range of human hearing
Ultrasonic sensor - sensor that uses sound to help robot determine distance
Condition - in programming it refers to the state of something which causes a decision to be made
Like a bat flying and navigating at night, which emits an ultrasonic frequency and calculates the distances of reflected sound to help it "see" in the dark, the ultrasonic sensor uses a sound reflection off an obstacle to help it determine range or distance to that obstacle. So the best use of an ultrasonic sensor is in detecting distance to an object.

Attach the Ultrasonic sensor to the front of BasicBot using the Technic™ liftarm 1x9 straight, two black friction pins and the Hassen pin, and connect the lead to default port 4.

Step 1

Step 2

Ultrasonic Sensor Exercise Distance Detection
Write a program using the ultrasonic sensor and the loop until the ultrasonic sensor will stop the robot when it is under eight inches from an object or wall.
Test it out on the side of a box. Does It work well? __Answer: Its not exact but close to eight inches when it stops.__ Now try the program again without the last MOVE block, which just stops it. Does it stop as well now? __Answer: It stops less than eight inches because it coasts more.__

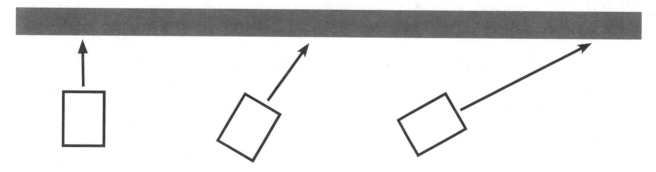

Test out the program on different angles against a wall or flat object. Does it always seem to stop at the correct distance? __Answer: The more angled to the wall it is the closer it stops, as the reflected signal may not be able to return to the sensor as effectively.__

Ultrasonic Sensor Exercise Collision Detection

Write a program that is similar to the Edge Detection program but uses the Ultrasonic sensor in front pointing straight ahead. This program will be called Collision Detection and will make the robot move forward until it encounters an obstacle eight inches away. Then it will back off and turn left/right and repeat.

Test it out on a object with a flat front. Then construct a polygon-shaped arena which has walls on all sides to test to see if this robot will move about the polygon without touching any of the walls.

Put two or more robots into the polygon and test them all at once.

This will look like an amusement park ride - the bumper cars, except that the cars try NOT to touch each other. Occasionally they will still bump and move away from each other.

The SWITCH Block

The SWITCH Block is basically a decision block, which means you are giving the robot the option of doing two different things based on a condition.

In the picture, the light sensor has a condition where if it is dark (value of less than 50), the robot will go forward and if the condition is bright (value of 50 or more), the robot will go backward for one rotation.

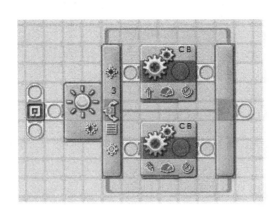

You have to choose your conditions carefully so they do not overlap. Also, you might have a case where only one condition is needed.

For example, you might just say "stop if the line is black" but have no condition if the line is white, as shown in the picture.

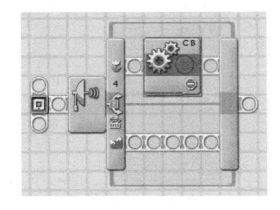

More Than One Condition

Many SWITCH Blocks can be included in a LOOP Block to check for multiple conditions. First build the manipulator for BasicBot using both the light sensor and the ultrasonic sensor.

Then write the following program. It is a loop which first makes the robot move forward indefinitely. Then it checks to see if the light sensor has found a black line and, if it did, then it stops. Note that there is no condition for white. It then also checks to see if the ultrasonic sensor is less than eight inches from an obstacle. If it is, then it stops; otherwise there is no negative condition. Then it loops and starts over.

Test the robot with a box and a black line. First put a black line about two inches from the box and send the robot towards the line. What happens? Answer: The robot stops.

Then put the black line eight inches away from the box and send the robot towards the line. What happens now? Answer: The robot also stops, but this time due to the light sensor.

Copyright © 2008 Technology Learning Classes for Kids

Manipulator with Light and Ultrasonic Sensors

Continuing from the previous page with just the Ultrasonic, add another Hassen pin, a liftarm L-shaped 2x4, two black friction pins and a blue axle pin. Then onto this attach the Light sensor which should be very close to the surface but not touching it.

 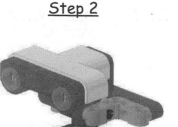

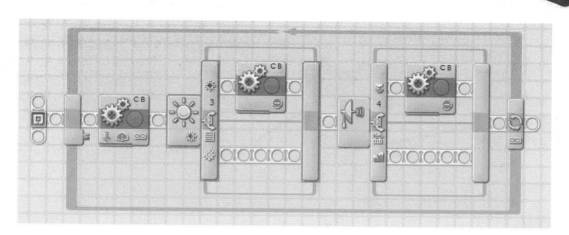

This kind of programming of conditions is called an "OR" condition, as the robot will stop when it either encounters a black line OR if a wall or object is detected within eight inches from the sensor.

Let's look at how you can best work with ultrasonic sensors and issues related to them.

Problems and Fixes for the Ultrasonic Sensor

Problems	Fixes
The robot hits at an angle	Select different path or select a flatter surface for signal
Other ultrasonic sensors are nearby	Will need to keep away from other ultrasonic sensors or use when they are not on
Sensor not stopping at correct distance	Might need to change position of the sensor. Maybe it is not directed to a flat surface. Note that the robot may be moving too fast towards the intended object so increase distance to stopping OR slow down the robot so that it registers the correct distance

Building the Lever-Based Manipulator

Build the manipulator shown in the picture and put it on the front of BasicBot.   The particular lever is used for delivering a specific item to a location. The "holding" portion of the manipulator has to be tailored to the shape and size of the item it is to deliver usually a bucket of some kind.

This manipulator is best used when you need to deliver an item that is at a height from the ground so that merely pushing the item to the target area will not work.   This would work for delivery to a hole, a ledge or shelf, or even a trough.

Care has to be taken to make the effort point (contact point) effective and reliable (always hitting on the same spot).   If not the item to be delivered may not drop into the right location.

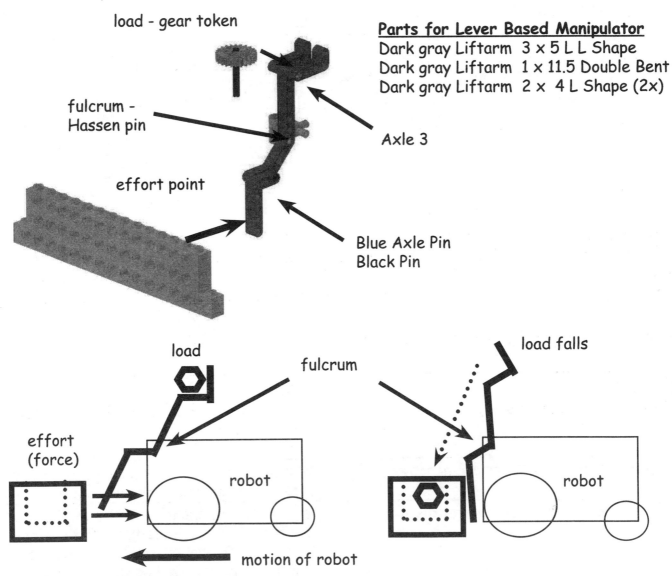

load - gear token

Parts for Lever Based Manipulator
Dark gray Liftarm 3 x 5 L L Shape
Dark gray Liftarm 1 x 11.5 Double Bent
Dark gray Liftarm 2 x 4 L Shape (2x)

fulcrum -
Hassen pin

Axle 3

effort point

Blue Axle Pin
Black Pin

load

fulcrum

load falls

effort
(force)

robot

robot

motion of robot

Mechanics of Lever-Based Manipulator

The most typical type of lever-based manipulator uses the first-class lever with the fulcrum (or pivot point) in the middle.   The contact with the target area will become the effort that pushes the lever arm so that the load (item to deliver) will then drop into the target location.

In the Hole Delivery Challenge

Build a robot to deliver a gear token to a square hole at the corner furthest from the base. You will have two chances to deliver this into a 6x7 bump hole, so with two of these starting in base, you have two opportunities.

You can borrow design plans from previous robot lessons.

Scoring

Competition will run for the entire class but each team will get two official tries only.
Each team gets 10 points for a working program that gets the robot close to the target.
Successful delivery of each gear token gets you 20 points each for a total of 40 points.

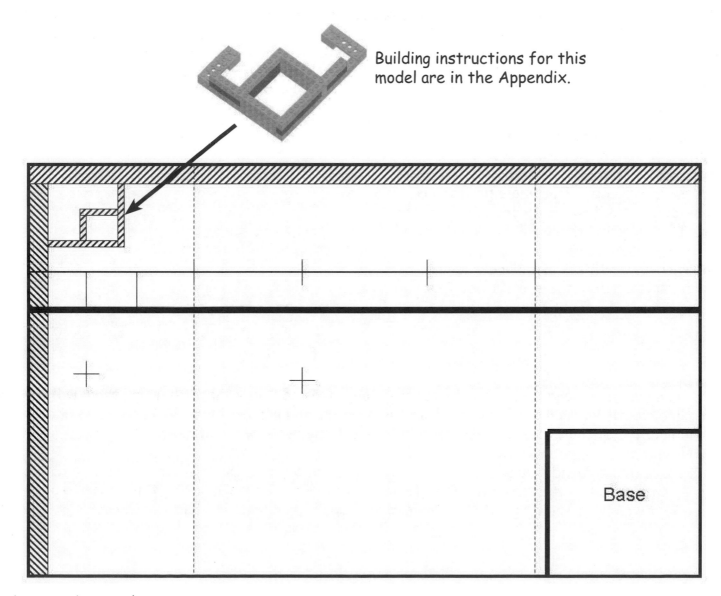

Building instructions for this model are in the Appendix.

Base

Lessons Learned

You can wrap-up the day with a discussion of the best manipulators or features of manipulators you have seen developed and some observations on how they might be improved even further.

Day 5
Introduction to the Sound Sensor

The sound sensor is a way for the robot to "hear" sounds in the environment and respond to them. The measurement of sound is usually in <u>decibels</u>.   The sensor, however, reports a percentage of sound in decibels back to the Intelligent Brick.

Typically, a reading of
4-5% is a silent living room,
5-10% is the sound of someone talking some distance away
10-30% is normal conversation or music at normal levels
30-100% the sound is of people shouting or music at high volumes

The typical way to use the sound sensor is to make the robot move or a motor run when a particular sound level has been reached. There are actually two kinds of sounds the sensor can detect - adjusted decibels, which is sound in the range of human hearing, and standard decibels, which includes sounds beyond the range that the ear can register and hear.

Sound Sensor Exercise - Basic Use

Write a program that will make your robot spin right/left only when the adjusted decibels is over 30 db.   The whole program is in a loop-forever so it will keep checking the sensor. If it is quiet, there will be no movement.

One way to use this is as a burglar alarm which rings a bell if the sound is loud enough.

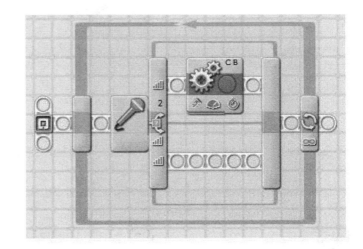

First connect the sound sensor to the robot.   You can place it anywhere that you think will work best in detecting a sound.   Then download the program and run it. Keep the room quiet and see if the robot stops moving.   Clap your hands to see if the robot will now move.

   I present the sound sensor here, but I have not seen any practical use of this sensor during FLL™ competition as the ambient noise of the competition area makes using this sensor a problem. So it's good to know that it's available, but teams typically do not use this sensor.

Introduction to the Touch Sensor

The touch sensor is a way for the robot to feel something. It has an orange tip that when pressed will send a signal which registers "1" to the Intelligent Brick. Otherwise, it registers as a zero signal.

There are three things you can test for in a touch sensor. You can see if the sensor has been "pressed" or "released" or just "bumped" (quick press and release).

The typical way to use a touch sensor is for detecting whether it has picked up something, or you can make the robot move only when the touch sensor has been pressed. One good thing to do is to increase the area where the sensor can be pressed by adding a larger surface to the front, for example an axle 2 with a 36-tooth double bevel gear.

Touch Sensor Exercise - Basic Use

Add both the sound sensor and a touch sensor to the front of the robot. Now write the following program, which loops forever and checks on the sensors. If the sound is louder than 30 db, then the robot moves forward one rotation, and if the touch sensor is pressed, then it moves backwards one rotation.

Test it out. Make enough noise for the robot to move forward, then put your hand in front of it to press the touch sensor.

Does the robot go backward immediately when you press the touch sensor?
Answer: Yes, it does.

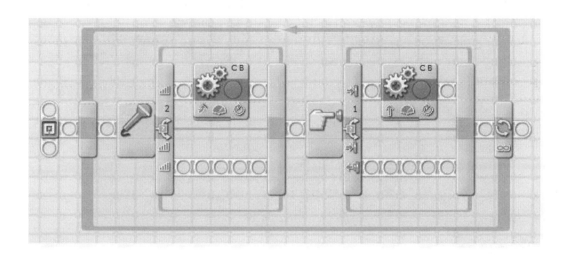

Tension Trigger Manipulator

A tension trigger manipulator is a lever that is kept in tension using a rubber band. A trigger is used to activate the lever when it is near or at the target object, which will then accomplish the mission.

   Because they are hard to design and use, these types of manipulators should be used sparingly. However, there are cases which warrant this manipulator - typically when the target or object is in a hard to reach location or at an odd angle for the robot to get to.

Building a Tension Trigger Manipulator

In this design, we have three parts to the manipulator, a strong frame, a trigger and a shooting arm, which is used to dislodge a target piece as part of the mission.   The trigger and the shooting arm work at right angles or at 90 degrees to each other.

   This example may NOT be the best manipulator for this mission. The mission is to travel from base to the far corner and knock the black angle connector #2 located on top of the corner model and hidden by light gray #3 connectors.   However, even if it is not the simplest solution, I am trying to show the concept of how the tension trigger manipulator might work.

Parts for the Shooting Arm
Axle 10 (3x)
Angle connector #2
Bushing
Half bushing (yellow)
Axle joiner perpendicular
Black pin long
Axle joiner double flexible

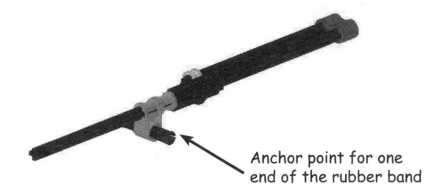

Anchor point for one
end of the rubber band

Parts for the Trigger
Axle 10, axle 3 and axle 2 (red)
Bushing
Half bushing (yellow, 2x)
Axle joiner perpendicular 3L
Black gear 36 double bevel
Technic cam wheel

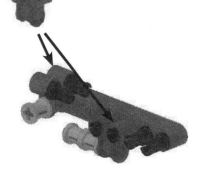

Parts for the Frame - Step 1
Axle joiner perpendicular double (2x)
Axle 3 with stud (2x)
Beam 7
Black pin (6x)
Bushing (3x)

Parts for the Frame - Step 2
Axle joiner perpendicular double
Axle joiner perpendicular
Axle 3 with stud, Axle pin
Beam 13
Black pin (5x), Bushing
Liftarm 2x4 L shape
Pin Joiner Perpendicular Bent

Anchor point for other
end of the rubber band

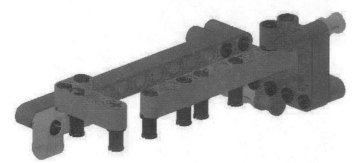

Parts for the Frame - Step 3
Axle pin
Beam 9
Black pin (5x)
Liftarm 2x4 L shape

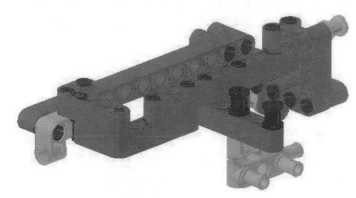

Parts for the Frame - Step 4
Black pin long with stop bush (2x)
Hassen Pin
Liftarm 3x5 L shape (2x)

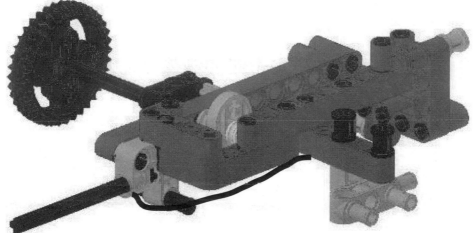

Tension Trigger Manipulator

Mechanics of This Tension Trigger Manipulator

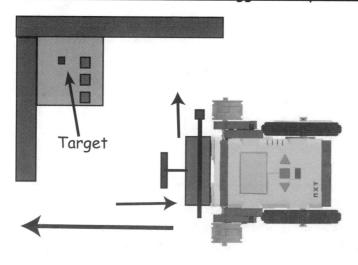

Target

This tension trigger is deployed in the front of the robot and as the robot approaches the side of the table, the trigger (black 36-tooth gear double bevel) is pushed in and releases the shooting arm, which fires at a right angle to the trigger and is positioned so that it only hits the intended target which in this case is the black angle connector #2.

As mentioned, the trigger works at a right angle to the shooting arm but that does NOT have to be the case in all tension triggers.

Hard to Reach Challenge

Build a robot that will knock down ONLY the two black #2 connectors and leave the other three gray #3 (pictured in dark gray but they are really light gray) connector pieces on the top of the obstacle, which itself is fixed on top of the "In the Hole" structure.
You can borrow design plans from previous robot lessons.

Scoring

Competition will run the entire class, but each team will get three official tries only.
Each team gets 10 points for a working program that gets the robot close to the target.
You get 20 points for each black connector #2 you knock down. If any gray #3 connector pieces fall over, you lose the previous points.

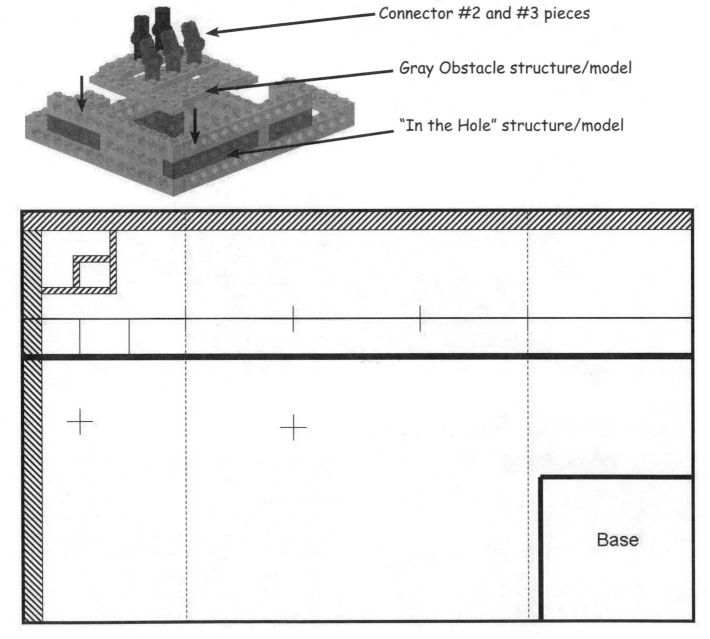

Connector #2 and #3 pieces

Gray Obstacle structure/model

"In the Hole" structure/model

Base

Lessons Learned

You can wrap-up the day with a discussion of the best manipulators or features of manipulators you have seen developed and some observations on how they might be improved even further.

Overview of Missions and Manipulators

Now that you have finished some basic missions, you can get a feel for the different types of missions. I believe that all missions can be classified into one of the three types listed below.

Summary of The Types of Missions

Trigger Missions
These missions typically involve moving to target area to hit/trigger an event.
For example:
- FLL™ 2005 Ocean Odyssey mission to release the trapped dolphin by hitting the trigger
- FLL™ 2006 Nano Quest mission to raise the Space Elevator
- FLL™ 2007 Power Puzzle mission to release the Solar Satellite panels.

Delivery Missions
There might be more variations in the delivery missions. One variation involves moving an item (token) from the base to target area.
For example:
- FLL™ 2007 Power Puzzle mission to move the Hydrogen Car to the house.
The second variation involves moving an item (token) from one target area to a second target area.
For example:
- FLL™ 2006 Nano Quest mission to move the pizza pieces from the starting pizza area to the LEGO® figure face.
The third variation involves moving the robot itself to the target area.
For example:
- FLL™ 2003 Mars Mission to get the All Terrain Vehicle (the robot) into the crater.
- FLL™ 2004 No Limits mission to get the robot up the stairs.

Retrieval Missions
These missions involve moving items (tokens) from a target area to the base.
For example:
- FLL™ 2005 Ocean Odyssey mission to get the shipping container and the cargo boxes from the ocean floor area to the base.

Also, since you have tried out some simple missions, we can generalize on the types of manipulators that you might have used in solving these missions.

Summary of Types of Manipulators
Each manipulator works well in a given situation and it is usually best to choose the simplest manipulator that can be built.   They are listed below in increasing order of difficulty to build.

1. Shaped Manipulator
This is the most basic manipulator and at its simplest can be nothing more than a stick.   However, it can take different shapes to allow it to move or deliver items to a target location, so it might have a T-shape, V-shape, or U-shape to conveniently guide an item along as the robot moves. It can also be used in trigger missions.

2. Center of Gravity (COG) -Based Manipulator
This manipulator has to be carefully constructed so that the COG will be placed just behind the base.   Then when the robot stops, the momentum of the manipulator will move the COG forward and down.

3. Lever-Based Manipulator
This manipulator is best used for delivering specific shaped objects. This manipulator is based on the lever, usually the first-class lever, which means the fulcrum will be in the middle.   The target object becomes the effort when the robot pushes forward, then the bucket at the other end will release an object onto the target.

4. Motorized Manipulator
This is a manipulator that we have not yet discussed.   Amazingly, many teams start out with this manipulator instead of waiting for a mission that might require it.   Also, some teams do a good job of making this a versatile manipulator that can be used in many missions.

   My own philosophy is that the motor is a high "cost" item, so if we can solve the mission without it, then we should do so. This is typically a manipulator, e.g. an arm or a hoop which is attached to the motor and is activated so that the motor slams the arm down to grab or hold the target.   It might be paired with sensors so that it triggers when the correct signal is sent to the sensors.   If this is used, I recommend that the attachments be made so that they can be interchanged with another one that can fit the motor easily, so that you can use the motors in multiple missions.   Also, some teams have the motor located on one side of the robot, which may cause some unintended friction or center of gravity issues. Center the motor on the robot if possible.

5. Tension Trigger-Based Manipulator
This is one of the hardest manipulators to build. The manipulator needs to be designed so that a trigger, which usually slides, will release a "lever" that is held in tension with a rubber band. This lever in turn either knocks something over or pushes something back.

6. Mothership-Podship Manipulator
This has not been discussed in any detail as it requires special pieces NOT found in the sets I have used for the camp.   However, the idea is that the robot acts as a mothership and it carries with it a manipulator which either uses a flywheel motor or a wind-up motor (found in many LEGO® racer sets).   The podship has a manipulator which is released outside of base (a requirement of the general rules of FLL™) and independently travels to the target to accomplish the mission. The release is critical, as the podship needs to proceed unhindered to the target. The program for release may need to be adjusted for a clean release.

Having an understanding of the types of missions and matching them with the appropriate type of manipulator may help the team move to a solution faster.

This ends the formal camp format for the book.   If you have a longer camp and you have a field mat and mission models from prior FLL™ years, you might want to set up the mat and have the team try out the basic methodologies you have taught.

There is a briefing page which I have titled "Essential Knowledge for All Team Members," which I use as a guide to ensure all team members have a good understanding before the season starts. The briefing will be found in the CD for this book.

Problem
Solving
Techniques
for
FLL™

"I hear and I forget, I see and I remember, I do and I understand."
- Chinese Proverb

Problem Solving

Problem solving is an art on which many books have been written. However, there are ways to improve one's ability, and I believe it is a question of training oneself to apply techniques which make sense.

Most people do not even know how to start applying knowledge they already. My best example of this is in solving puzzles.

The following is a puzzle you can make by simply photocopying the page (preferably on hard stock paper) and then cutting out the pieces. There are four pieces which make a large square and a single piece which is a smaller square. The problem is simple: use all five pieces to make a larger square.

The only hint I will give you is that this can be solved by using simple geometry, and your time limit for solving this should be five minutes. When I say "geometry" to my students, most of them wrinkle their noses at me as if to say, "What do you mean use geometry,".

Another common comment I hear is, " I hate geometry." But what if I said you can solve this using common sense? I do not think they will turn around and say, "I hate common sense."

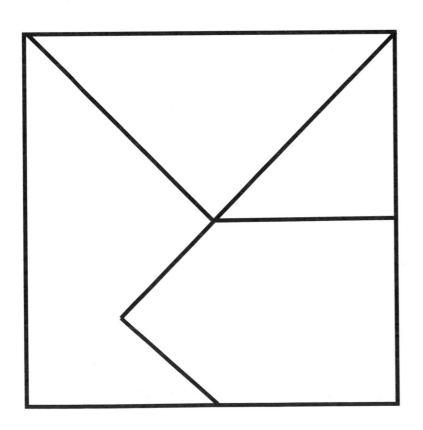

Most people will use the trial and error method and start jamming pieces together to see if they can work it out on the fly. Some of this is an underestimation of the puzzle's complexity, i.e. believing that five pieces cannot be very difficult to work out.
However, if we just apply some math to the puzzle, a quick and dirty calculation of the number of possible combinations of pieces might be reached by just multiplying the number of sides of all the pieces together.

Number of possible combinations = 3 x 3 x 4 x 5 x 5 = 900 combinations.

So even if a person was able to test out one combination a second, it would take you 900/60 or 15 minutes to test out all combinations, which is too long over the time limit.
So how can you use geometry to solve this?

Let's start with basic knowledge about squares. One basic property of a square is that all four sides of the square are equal in length. Also, we know that if the new square uses all five pieces of the puzzle instead of just the original four pieces, then the new square MUST be larger. And therefore, the sides of the new square must be longer than the original.

In fact, from the above illustration, we can see that if we could somehow melt down the material in the small original square and pad it to just two sides of the original square, we could have the solution. But that is not possible.
So where do we go from here? We simply have to find a side in the new square that is longer than the sides in the old square. From the picture of the original square, you can see which of the pieces make up two of the sides of the original square - the long side of the odd shaped piece and the long side of the large triangle.

A natural fit is the small square in the notch of the odd piece. When we then test the long side against the original side (long side of the large triangle), we see it is indeed a bit longer.

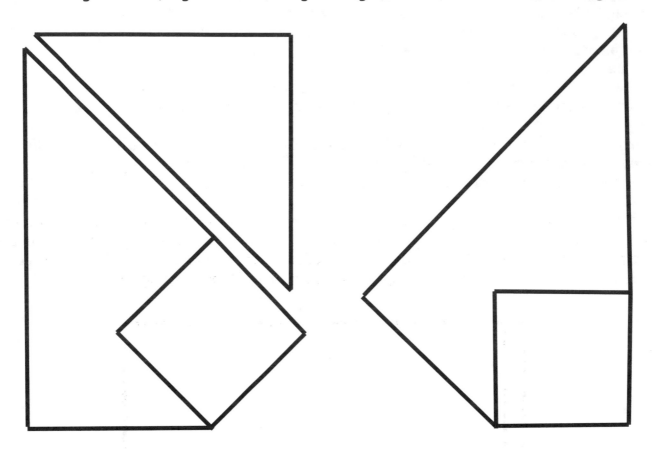

So we now know one of the sides of the new square.   Only three pieces need to be placed to solve the puzzle.   The next piece that can be derived from geometry is the bottom side. We must find a piece that will continue the small square and be another of the longer sides.

In this case the only piece that fits that description is one of the shorter side of the large triangle.   See illustration here.

All that is left are the two pieces, one in the shape of a house and one small triangle.

At this point you should be able to figure it out easily.

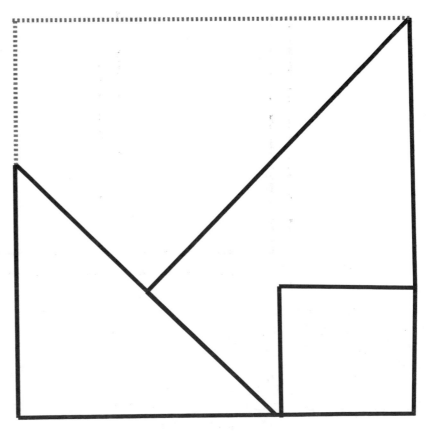

So here we have the final solution.

The slightly tricky part is in realizing that the house shaped piece has the pointed end making two corners of the new larger square.

Again, the geometry used to solve this was not complicated.

Were you able to apply it?
How structured were you on the solution?
Did you solve it in the time limit?
Did you have to peek at some hints to get you started?

Once again, the solution was found through simple reasoning, or geometry, or common sense.

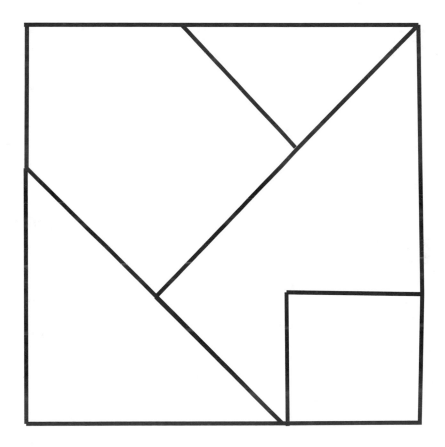

What does this tell us?
It tells us that most people, especially students, are not trained or prepared to use knowledge they already possess in problem solving. Some of the problem is that they have not been taught techniques for applying what they already know.

Planning Prototypes

In planning the prototype, I usually like to think of the three Ps which are path, program and pieces. The path is the most important item to work out, as it determines how to get your robot to the target area or where the action will take place. The path usually then dictates the program. Simple paths will have simple programs and more complex paths will have more complex programs. Finally, when the team is able to get the robot to the target, then the design of the manipulator to be deployed determines the pieces used.

The area that I will be concentrating the rest of this chapter on is in the initial design of manipulators and the refinements a team has to go through to make the deployed manipulator reliably solve missions. There may be times when the design of the manipulator may cause a change in the design of the robot, but if teams plan ahead, there should be few issues here. A typical example might be that the manipulator may need to be attached at a specific point on the robot which necessitates creating areas of attachment or moving pieces so that the manipulator can be accommodated in that particular attachment point on the robot.

Path and Path Selection

Path selection is usually the first thing in solving a mission. It is important because it can change the entire approach to a solution.

The position where the robot ends up near the target determines where the manipulator is situated on the robot body. For example, the manipulator can be situated on the left side, the right side, the front top, the front bottom, the back of the robot, in the middle, etc. Each of these manipulator locations will then determine how close the robot gets to the target or even which side of the target the robot needs to move to.

Let us first consider each mission as a problem with three separate components:
- Get the robot to the target area
- Deploy/Use/Trigger the manipulator
- Return the robot back to base (optional)

Breaking it down this way allows the team members to reduce the complexity so that solutions will become more apparent. The first and third components are linked, as they are dependent on selecting the path of the robot. There are times when you might not return the robot to base, e.g. if it is the last mission to be attempted or if the rules permit it, which would make the path a one-way trip.

Good Questions to Ask Team Members About Path Selection

How do you get the robot to the target?
Does the path consists of forward and backward motion or are turns involved?
What are good ways of simplifying the path to the target?
What edges/walls can you use as a reference/guide?
Will this path interfere with another mission? How can we avoid that?

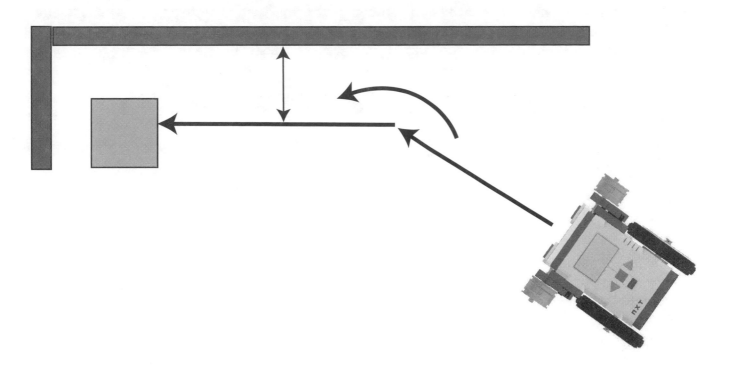

In the above example mission, the robot has to move from where it is located to the final position to the right of the target in order to deploy a manipulator.   The path here is fairly easy to work out.

One reason is that the target is set a some distance from the wall at the edge, which gives the robot some room to work. The path also has only one turn, so it should be easy to program.

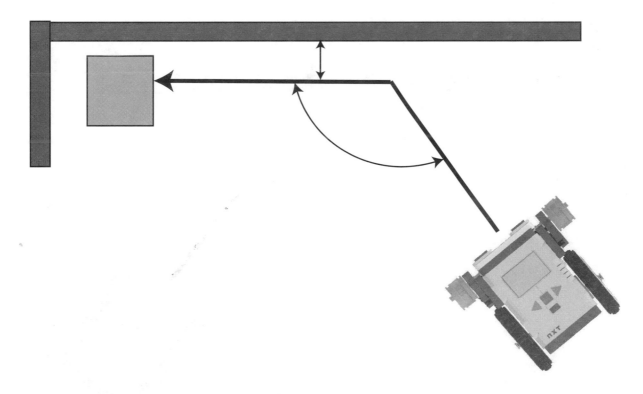

However, complications come into play in this next example.   The target is now closer to the edge and so the turn angle is larger.

When the target is closer to the wall edge, the angle of the turn is tighter, and because the wheels are in the back of the differential drive as it pivots about the left wheel, indicated by the star below, the front of the robot gets in the way of the turn.

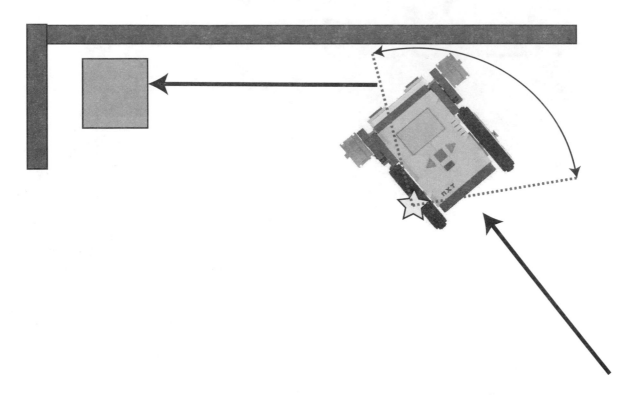

This problem usually becomes more apparent when a test program has been run and we see the right side hitting the wall and getting stuck.

So how do we solve this path issue? We can try starting with a backward move.

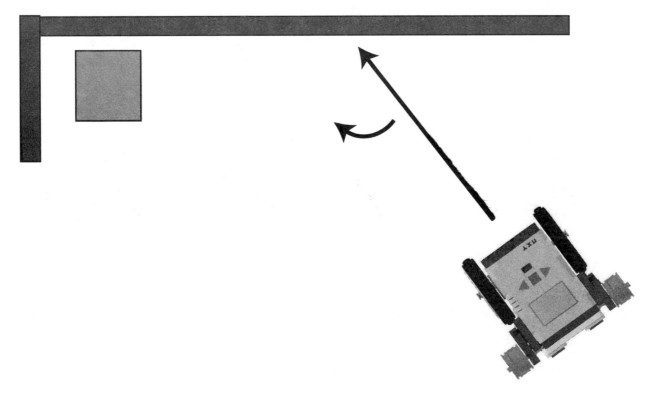

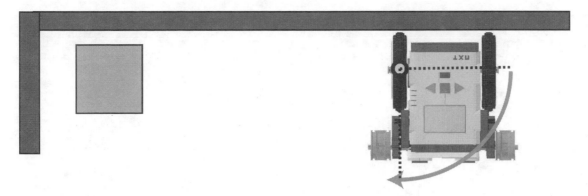

When the back of the robot hits the wall, we allow it to square itself to the wall. This can be done easily by making the program that makes the robot go backward exceed the distance to the wall.   Simply add more seconds on the backward motion after the robot hits the wall.

Notice that this uses the wall as a reference or landmark by deliberately allowing the robot to square itself to the wall.   In effect, the path from this point by the wall is like a new path, because we know that we will have a robot with its back square to the wall.

We then program another MOVE Block to turn the robot towards the target this time by pivoting on the right wheel.   This turn path is shown with the light gray arrow in the picture above.

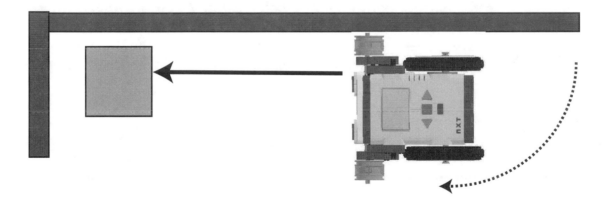

The final move is simply to go forward to the target.

The important part here is the technique of using the walls as a reference point. Veteran teams use this a lot, especially when the path to the target is more convoluted or requires a lot of turns or is in tight spots. The intermediate locations against a wall make it seem as if the robot will have a fresh start from that position by the wall. Sometimes not just walls but the mission target itself or other mission models that lie along the way can be the reference point.

There are different ways to solve this.   Another solution is simply to make two turns - an intermediate turn to create some room, then a final turn to get it towards the target. However, I believe that more turns in a program will cause more issues, as this reduces the predictability of the path to the target.   Also, there may not be enough room to make two turns.

So the wall reference technique is a good one to use.

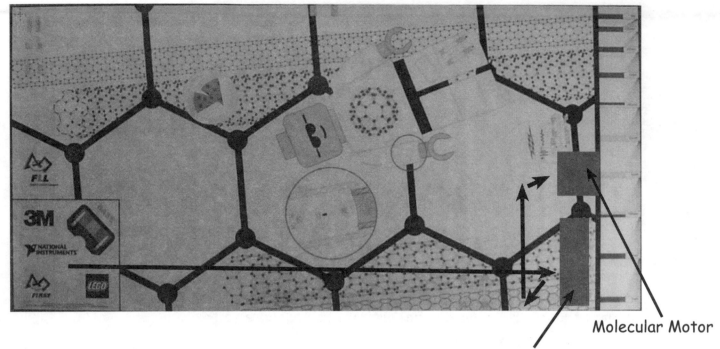

Molecular Motor

Self-Assemblying
Nano Tube

Example with Two Intermediate Stops

Here is an example of a complex path from the FLL™ 2006-7 season, where the robot came out of base and used the mission model Self-Assembling Nano Tube as a stop, then backed into a wall to square off against it, then went forward and turned right to get to the Molecular Motor mission model. Each stop was used to alter a complex path into a manageable one.

The Inverse View for Paths

Another way to determine the path is to start the robot at the target first, then drag it backward from the target back to the launch point in base. This sort of "reverse engineering" may be useful, as it may also reveal other angles or paths not previously thought out.

Creative Problem Solving Techniques for Missions

"To live a creative life, we must lose our fear of being wrong.
- Joseph Chilton Pearce

Creative Problem Solving Techniques

Let's look at some techniques for generating ideas. In the summer of 2004, I decided that I needed to teach other techniques to team members rather than just relying on the age-old method of brainstorming solutions in the group. So I read through the book *101 Creative Problem Solving Techniques* by J.M. Higgins, which summarized many techniques in the hopes that I would find some that could be adapted easily to solving FLL™ missions. By the end of that summer, many of the techniques started sounding similar

But I found six techniques that can be useful in coming up with alternative ideas.

How Do You Get the Next Idea/Alternative in an Iterative Process?

Analysis of Past Solutions (should be the first and obvious choice)
Brainstorming (likely the most common technique, good for groups)
Brain writing (variation of Brainstorming, good for groups)
Attribute Listing (my favorite among this bunch)
Morphological Analysis (variation of Attribute Listing)
Orthogonal Thinking (borrowed from business strategy class)

Analysis of Past Solutions

Veteran teams can look at previous missions that have a similarity to the current mission and see what they have tried in past years. Choose that as an initial starting point and start iterations. For new teams, attend local and state competitions to learn from the other teams. Watch videos online of past competitions. There are some great links from the European FLL™ Championships on the FIRST® LEGO® League™ web site, and links to other web sites showing past year solutions. I also keep a box of past "great" solutions which are generic enough to team members and help them remember those solutions.

Brainstorming

This concept was invented by Alex Osborn of the advertising firm of Batten, Barton, Durstine and Osborn to increase the quantity and quality of advertising ideas. It was called "brainstorming" because participants' brains were used to "storm" a problem. Usually groups offer alternatives orally and spontaneously which are then written down. Wild ideas are encouraged and quantity is paramount. Ideas are then sifted through and evaluated by the group. Usually rules and expectations are set up front – the most common one is that "Suggestions are not pre-judged." It is a good idea to have a whiteboard or other writing area that everyone can view when brainstorming.

Brain writing

Similar to brainstorming but nonverbal. Participants sit in a circle and write down ideas, which are then passed clockwise to their neighbor, and other ideas are piggy-backed on for a specified time. A possible two or three exchanges are made to generate many ideas. It has the advantage of the leader's not being too influential, but it is less spontaneous than brainstorming. It presumes good communication skills (also good hand writing skills). Also, the ideas need to be sketched, so that presumes all members have good drawing and communication skills.

> **Tip:** Use Analysis of Past Solutions, Brainstorming & Brain writing as starting points for solutions.

Attribute Listing
Developed by Professor Robert Platt Crawford of the University of Nebraska. Start by listing all attributes or qualities of a problem or object. Systematically analyze each attribute or group of attributes and try to change them in as many ways as possible. Then review the resulting attributes for practical and best solutions.

In the attributes listed below, some possible changes are in the brackets. Test each of the changes to see if something needs to be altered for a particular attribute. Applying this to the Sample Species mission, we changed the Contact Region attribute from a point of contact to a longer line of contact in the second solution. In the final solution, we changed the Impact with Target from hard to soft.

Manipulator Attributes
- Dimensions – length, width, height (increase/decrease)
- Weight - payload (increase/decrease)
- Attachment Point to Robot (right/left, front/back, top/bottom, at an angle)
- Sensor triggers attachment (yes/no). If yes, will you use light sensor/touch sensor.
- Impact with Target (hard/soft)
- Contact Place on Target (right/left, front/back, top/bottom, at an angle)
- Contact Region with Target (point, line, area)
- Center of gravity of the robot and manipulator together
- Friction on contact of the manipulator

A listing can also be found in the Appendix for you to photocopy and give out to your team members to use. Again, the idea is that for each manipulator trial, team members observe the results, then go through the listing to determine which ones have issues.
For example, for each mission you would ask:
Is the length of the manipulator causing a problem?
Is the width of the manipulator causing a problem?
Is the contact region with the target appropriate?

Of course, this can become tedious, but it is structured and comprehensive. Also, as team members get better, they can skip over some questions and ask more appropriate ones.
These questions are geared toward the manipulator but sometimes its the path of the robot which needs to be altered to better solve a mission, or some other attribute not relating to the manipulator only.

Morphological Analysis
This technique was developed by Fritz Zwicky, a famous astronomer who helped discover quasars. It uses a matrix where the items on the horizontal axes are attributes (factors, objectives in other problems) and those on the vertical axes are characteristics, adverbs, adjectives, prepositions, etc. We try to force one set of characteristics against another to create new ideas. Choice of the characteristics is important, as you want those that can give you new insights. The big advantage of morphological analysis is that it generates a lot of ideas in a short time.

You can use this in a group or individually, then develop a pooled matrix.

Morphological Analysis Table for FLL™ Manipulator

	Adapt	Modify	Duplicate	Add to	Increase	Decrease	Substitute	Rearrange	Reverse	Combine	Yes / No	Switch Side	Take apart
Length													
Width													
Height													
Weight													
Attachment Point to Robot													
Sensor Triggers Attachment													
Impact with Target													
Contact Place on Target													
Contact Region with Target													
Path to Target													

Orthogonal Thinking

This is one of my favorite ways of generating ideas. I remember using this in a business strategy class. The idea is to look at the opposite elements in a particular corporation to try to discover what the new business can become or what it might be missing. For instance, in the class we talked about whether the business was vertically integrated or horizontally stratified. Did it sell goods to the public sector or the private sector? Was the income from the business fixed fee-based or commission-based? Then we talked about whether the corporation needed to go into areas where it was not currently involved.

So the idea is to deliberately look at the opposite elements from how you are approaching a problem to see if this can give you some insight into a new approach. Roger von Oech talks of reversing your viewpoint and writes, "Doing the opposite of what's expected can also be an effective strategy in competitive situations such as sports, business, warfare, romance, etc."

In the next section, we will look at examples of how these problem-solving techniques were applied to solving missions.

Sample Solutions from Previous FLL™ Missions

"If the only tool you have is a hammer, you tend to see every problem as a nail."   - Abraham Maslow

Sample Species Mission

The following pages detail FLL™ missions from previous years that might be useful in inspiring your team when they are solving missions.

Let's look at the sample species mission and the iterative process to solve it. The figure below is a top view of the FLL™ 2005 Ocean Odyssey competition mat, which is four feet by eight feet with mission elements on it. The Sample Species Mission has the objective of tagging the gray fish while leaving the three green fish untouched. The path is a simple one, with a straight line from base at an angle and, after tagging the gray fish only (second from the left), the robot has to return to base by reversing the motors or going backward. The starting solution does not have to be complicated. I encourage the simplest – a simple stick (extended axle).

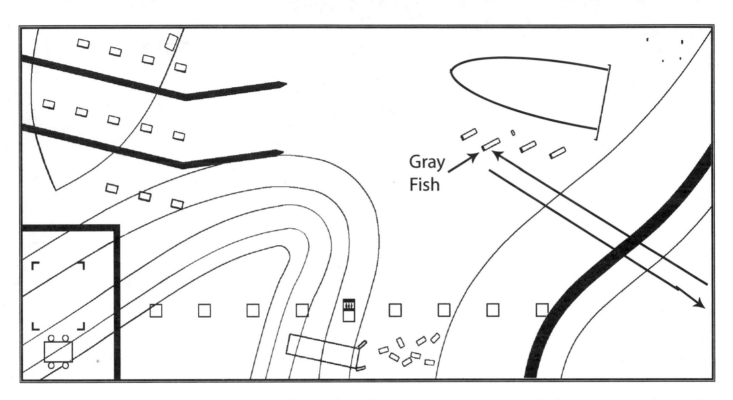

Gray Fish

After testing and evaluating the simple stick, ask your team members, "What can you do to the simple stick to make it a better solution?" Note that in the second iteration, we change the contact with the target from a point (end of stick) to a line (higher probability of hitting the target).

This next section shows the evolution or iteration of ideas to get to a better solution.

Initial Solution

Issue:

Need better contact with target

2nd Solution

Contact Area

Issue:

Too hard contact with target

In this simple mission with two iterations or improvements from the initial solution, we manage to get to a good solution.

Final Solution

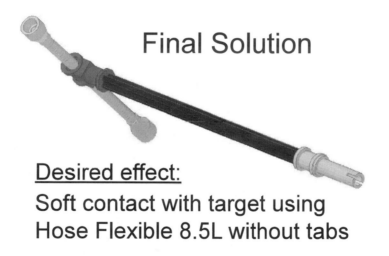

Desired effect:

Soft contact with target using Hose Flexible 8.5L without tabs

However, here's another point of view of the fish to generate more ideas. The gray fish at its highest point is three plates (shown by the white and black plates below) higher than the green fish. Manipulators that are positioned high could easily move the gray fish by nudging the gray fish's tail without disturbing the green fish. This would have the advantage of not needing as precise a manipulator to contact the gray fish.

three plates added to show height difference

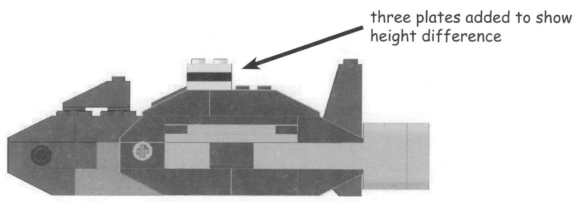

Application of Attribute Listing

Dolphin and Pipeline Mission,

The objectives of these missions are to free the dolphin from the sling and to install the missing section of the pipeline. The first is accomplished by using a front manipulator (like a bumper), then backing up and pushing the missing pipe piece to complete the pipeline using the back end of the robot as a back bumper. This path is a somewhat complicated one, with a straight line from base at an angle, then a right turn and stopping appropriately after it hits the sling, then backing up perpendicular to the long edge of the table until it hits the pipeline, moving forward again a short distance before a final right turn, and forward to take it back to base.

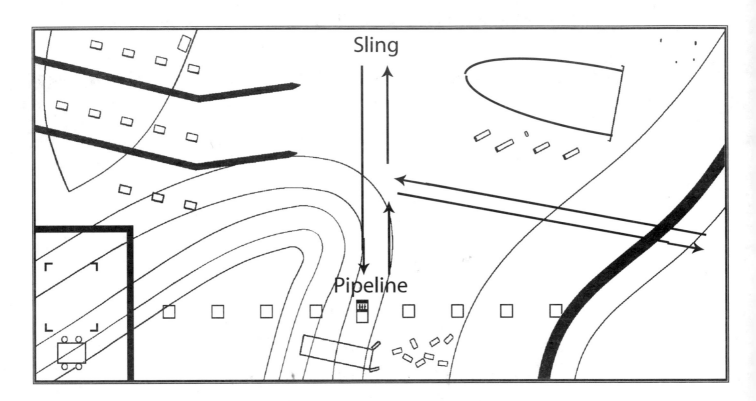

The initial solution was arrived at quickly with just a simple bumper made of beams. As an extreme case of always starting with the simplest, if the team started with just the extended axle, an iteration would have added the front bumper to have better contact, and a second iteration might have modified the back attachment point so it has two pins to attach to the robot front, which will improve the stability of the bumper.

Initial Solution

Issue:
Front contact area
still too small

Copyright © 2008 Technology Learning Classes for Kids

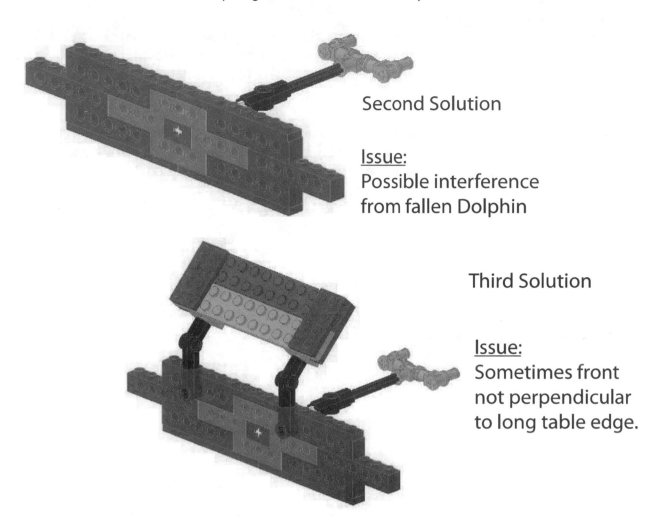

Second Solution

Issue:
Possible interference from fallen Dolphin

Third Solution

Issue:
Sometimes front not perpendicular to long table edge.

Although the team developed a "Dolphin Catcher"or deflector, this was ultimately not used, as the rules allowed teams to ask the table referees to remove the dolphin after it was freed, and the deflector would have added to the weight of the manipulator.

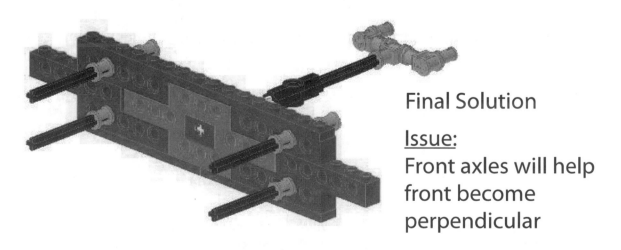

Final Solution

Issue:
Front axles will help front become perpendicular

Looking at the path, the first right turn is important because, if made incorrectly, then the robot path will not be perpendicular to the long edge of the table. Our robot uses a timer in Robolab to make turns, which is not precise, so using these four axles will make the robot square to the edge.

Application of Orthogonal Thinking

The mission where the team had the most fun with this technique was the Container and Cargo Mission. The team found that looking at the orthogonal elements was helpful, i.e., push vs. pull, back vs. front, outside vs. inside. This led to various options to try out and evaluate.

Container and Cargo Mission

The objective here was to get the container and cargo boxes back to base. Let's ignore the cargo at this point. The biggest problem was the container, which was a heavy payload to return to base. The path from base is very simple and noted below.

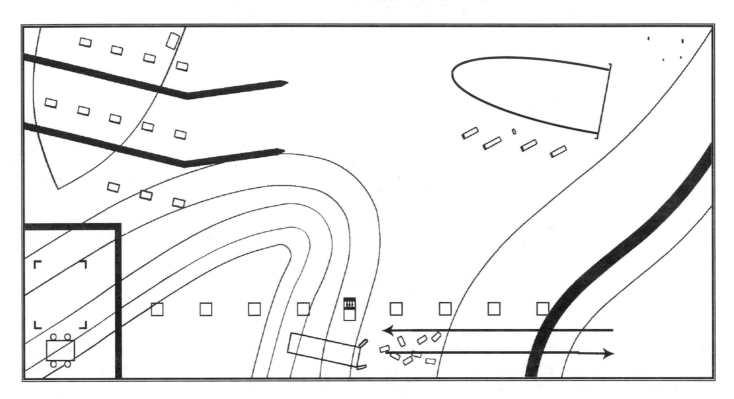

The first option is to get a long "lasso" to drop around the back of the container so we could pull it into base. Some issues were that the lasso needed to be light and could not exceed the height limit for any manipulator on the robot. Also, the lasso had a tendency to either slip off the back because of the heavy container weight or sometimes not deploy properly.

As we tried out options for the missions, the team members started to play with the words to help promote orthogonal trials:

Pull versus pull
Inside versus outside
Front versus back

Combinations of these words helped us form various options and develop manipulators that all work in very different ways, eventually arriving at an easy yet effective solution.

> **Tip:** Use Attribute Listing, Morphological Analysis and Orthogonal Thinking to make adjustments to get to final solutions.

Option 1
Pull from back

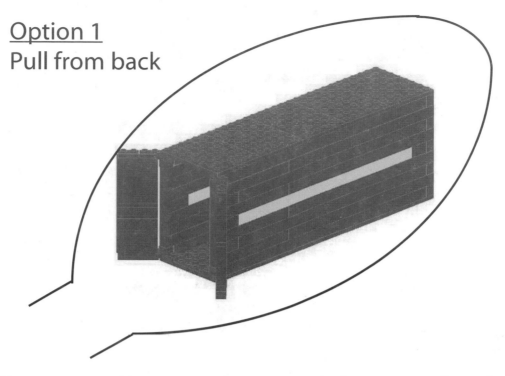

The second option was to consider some mechanism to grab the container from the inside front. The mechanism was fairly complex, involving worm gears and a motor and worked less than half the time.   It was also harder to reset to make trials.

Option 2
Pull from inside front

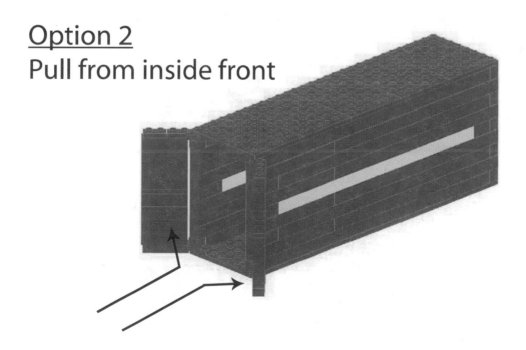

The option that worked and was most reliable was to have a mechanism to grab the container from the front. Again the weight of the container was an issue, so there was a tendency for the forked grabbing arms to slip up and off. However, a pawl and ratchet built into the drop-down mechanism overcame this issue.

Option 4
Pull from outside front

Ratchet Locks
Grabbing Arm
Once Down

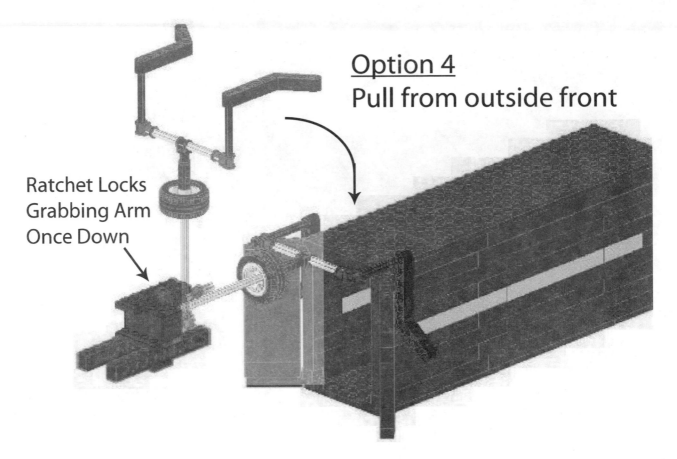

Here is a close-up of the ratchet with some pieces removed to show how the mechanism worked. As the large grabbing arm fell, it would drag on the bushing noted below which acted as a pawl to the 24-tooth ratchet gear.

Close-up of Pawl and Ratchet
The bushing here is used as a pawl on the ratchet (24-tooth gear) and locks it in place.

Raise the Rows of Flags and Protect Pump Station Mission

The objectives here were to raise all the flags on each of the three rows and to push a protective structure over the pump station. The team was only able to work out a reliable solution for one row of flags. This was the one mission for us that dictated more programming. The original plan was to go straight to the short edge of the table and on the way use flexible axles on the right-hand side to brush the flags up. There would be a rolling cart that would trigger a "hammer" perpendicular to the edge of the table and push the protective structure over the pump station. This would make the path simple to program but the hammer was not reliable, plus the cart had to navigate over a long distance through a very narrow pass between the flags and the pipeline. The flags portion of the mission worked, but pushing the protective structure was unreliable and the narrow path made for a narrow cart, which was unstable.

Here a complete rework was needed, and the other choice that was brought up was a complex change to the path.

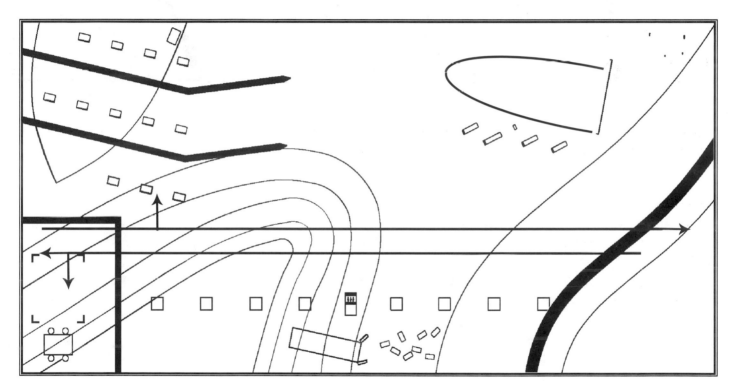

So the team changed the path to make use of the black lines, which then necessitated a line follower program which they were able to write using Robolab 2.5.4. It was still a straight line shot from base, but at an angle to allow the light sensor to read the lower black line. From then on the robot followed the line till it reached the edge of the table. On the way, it would use the Technic Flexible Axles to brush the flags up on the left-hand side. There were two flexible axles one in the middle of the robot and one at the back. The front flexible axle would raise the flag, the back flexible axle would keep it up while the front flexible axle raised the next one in the sequence. Some initial missed readings of the black line were overcome by a hooded or shielded light sensor. The shot out of base was made more reliable with a jig to help position the robot. Finally two more flexible axles were attached to the very front of the robot as whiskers to increase contact with the protective structure as the robot pushed it over the pump station.

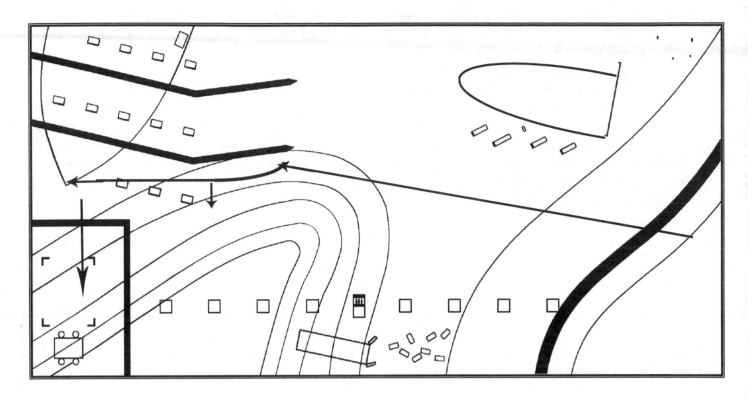

Here, the final solution involved changing the path to the target area, and also involved switching to a more sophisticated program which incorporated a line follower.

Summary

I presented six techniques that can be used to generate new ideas especially to affect manipulator design. I recommend using Analysis of Past Solutions, Brainstorming and Brain writing initially with the entire group to generate ideas for prototypes.

Then in smaller groups or individually, use Attribute Listing, Morphological Analysis and Orthogonal Thinking to help refine prototypes and iterate into better solutions.

Now that you have some missions solved, let's talk about what you need to do to prepare for a full run of all the missions on the table for Robot Performance.

Preparation
for
Running
FLL™
Missions

"There are no secrets to success. It is the result of preparation, hard work and learning from failure." - Colin Powell

Sequencing

Sequencing the missions is critical to the success of a strong robot performance score. The approach is to try to sequence with the intent of getting a better score.
Here are some considerations for sequencing.

Some missions are done first because there are bonus points for completing that mission before the opposing team completes it.

Some missions are to be done last as there may not be a round trip, i.e., the robot is left where it is at the end of the table run.   This is usually appropriate for missions that are furthest away from base and that require no delivery back to base.

Some missions must be done before another mission is accomplished, otherwise a strategic object (manipulator) or other mission props may be in the way of another future mission.

Sometimes it is better to do one side of a table first to allow for smoother flow of missions.

Start the sequencing with the missions you already know will have to be first or last and then fill in the sequence with the missions that make the most sense in the flow of manipulators.

Practice and Transitions

There is NO substitute for practice.   The only way a team will get better is to practice the sequence of missions over and over again, so lots of time will have to be allocated to make this work.
    The other reason to practice is that doing so will reveal the robust missions and the weak missions. During the frantic pace of getting manipulators onto the robot and running the programs, you will likely discover that some missions will still work when the positioning of the robot is slightly off from the ideal starting point. However, there will be missions that will be extremely touchy or sensitive to small changes in position. It is these missions, then, that your team will need to rework and figure out how to make into robust missions.

A simple measure of the robustness of the mission is just repeating it a set number of times to observe success and failure.
If the mission succeeds 9 out of 10 times, then it is robust.
If the mission succeeds 4 out of 5 times, then it is satisfactory.
If the mission succeeds 2 out of 3 times or less, then it needs work.

The other area for adjustments comes in the transitions between the missions. Each time a robot exits base, it is typically able to accomplish multiple missions. Sometimes it makes sense to just do one mission at a time, but the time limit of 2.5 minutes usually means you need to combine two or three missions per program, especially for the missions that are grouped together and far from base and take the longest time.
    I propose timing a full table run from the beginning to the end and noting the time using a stop-watch.
    On the next page I have an example of a full table run with missions, each of the seconds elapsed from zero, and each time when the robot exits the base or returns to base till the end of the round.

Example of FLL™ 2005 Ocean Odyssey Mission Runs and Transitions

0 s	Mission Runs	Time(s)	Notes
	Missions - Free Dolphin and Setup Pipeline	10	
m. 10 s.			
	Time in Base	10	
m. 20 s.			
	Missions - Tag Gray Fish	10	
m. 30 s.			
	Time in Base	15	
m. 45 s.			
	Missions - Retrieve Coral	30	
1 m. 15 s.			
	Time in Base	15	
1 m. 30 s.			
	Missions - Get Container and Cargo Boxes	20	
1 m. 50 s.			
	Time in Base	25	
2 m. 15 s.			
	Missions - Raise row of flags and cover station	15	
2 m. 30 s.			

Column 1 above is the elapsed time from zero, and each time a robot exits base or returns to base.   Column 2 is a description of the missions attempted in that trip.   Column 3 uses column 1 to calculate the difference in time elapsed. Column 4 is used for notes.

From the above results, we can determine that the mission combination that took the longest was Program 3, Retrieve Coral, and the worst transition was between Program 4 and Program 5.   There are likely ways to make the mission solutions shorter.   Also, there are likely ways to reduce the transition time.   Some ways are to place the manipulators in a more convenient position, changing the attachment points for the manipulator, putting the programs in mission sequence order, and also practicing the choreography of the missions.

   A blank form for the mission runs and transitions can be found in the Appendix and on the enclosed CD.

I usually only start practicing a full run when at least half the missions have been solved. However, some teams may never be able to solve more than just a few missions.

Who Gets to Run the Table?
This is one of the most important things to work out. I try to get the team to see that the table operators will determine the Robot Performance score, so the team needs to work out who will serve them best.

Pros and Cons of Many Operators vs. Two Persons Only
If you allow many table operators, then more team members get to participate in this most exciting part of the tournament.   However, swapping many operators in and out may cause lost time. Two operators can be more efficient.

When practicing, if many operators are involved, and one is absent, that may throw off the practice.   With fewer operators, practices can be scheduled for just the operators when tournaments get closer so that they can benefit from the extra practice. Also, fewer operators mean that each operator will have more things to remember and work during the missions.

Assignment of Roles During Practice
Assign roles to team members according to how they can contribute. Not everyone can be at the table running the missions. I prefer to have only two operators but may have a primary team of two members and a backup team of two members.   I believe it does take a special person to be a good table operator.   That person has to be quick at grasping the situation, memorizing lots of details of programs to run and positioning of manipulators, have the ability to work well with another team member and also be able to think quickly on their feet in case things go wrong.

I then ask one person to help be in charge of the stopwatch, and another member be in charge of the form for the timing of missions and transitions when needed.   The other team members can still participate, by resetting sections of the table as needed between runs so we can make as many practices as possible and also keeping a sharp lookout during runs for any kind of improvements that can be made.

Once missions are stabilized, it does not mean there can't be further improvement.   My team members usually keep working on improvements all the way to the start of the tournament. However, we tend to make fewer improvements towards the end. Ultimately, the operators who do best on the table are those who practice the most.

Contingency Planning
A contingency is a "Plan B" in case Plan A does not work. Quite frequently in solving missions, the solution does not go the way you thought it would or the robot does something unexpected. Some preparation may help in recovering from a bad situation or missed opportunity.

It is impossible to think of all the possible contingencies that might happen, but some things should be worked out in advance so that table operators do not have to work them out on the fly.

One mission in FLL™ 2007 Power Puzzle was to deliver the Wave Turbine to the ocean area east of the beach. If the original wave turbine could not be delivered, some teams had figured out that they would simply deliver the robot itself and declare that as the Wave Turbine. The criterion for the turbine was that it must have two pieces that moved independently of each other, which any robot would qualify.   Note that this would be a last-ditch effort and the last mission, as the robot would be left in the ocean area.

Another example is related to how well you can read the rules and use them to your advantage. There were many multi-part missions in the FLL™ 2007 Power Puzzle season. The mission goal was to move all the Corn pieces to base. The corn in its target (base) is worth 20 points if at least one Oil Barrel has been moved to the Farm. One team accomplished this by using a hoop to drag all the corn back to base, then push out the red truck with one oil barrel in it. However, there were times when a corn piece would fall down and be left on the Farm. But the team still dutifully delivered the oil barrel to the farm. Looking at the scores, if the team retrieved all the corn and pushed the barrel out to the farm it would receive 20 points. However, as soon as the robot was unable to get all the corn, the team lost the opportunity for the 20 points. But pushing out the Oil Barrel at that point meant that the team also lost 10 more points for an oil barrel at base. Once one condition was not able to be met (missed corn), the oil barrel would be better served by leaving it back at base. This way there would have been only 10 missed points instead of 30.

Sometimes when an item is being pushed out of base, it goes off the planned route enough to be a problem or cause lost points. Examples might include, in the FLL™ 2007-8 season, delivering the wind turbine to any white area not directly outside base or the dam so it was touching both banks of the river section east of base. The flood upstream of the dam should not touch any house or there would be a 10-point deduction. If something did not position correctly, it might have been worth it, if time permitted, to send the robot out again to help nudge the item to the correct position. Some programs for other missions might be adapted to do this. But it is a good idea to test out a few scenarios.

Again, it is not essential to try to think of all the contingencies. And I think it is foolish to spend a lot of time on contingency planning, but some quick sensible plans in place may mean the difference between a solved mission and a missed opportunity.

Past Winning Strategies
The following is a discussion of many strategies that I make known to my team members, because many top teams use them to good effect, and year after year they are applied to many mission solutions.

Full Understanding of the Rules
Just as in any sport you play in, you MUST know the rules and understand how to maximise the score in the game. One exercise I get the team to do is to place all the items in all the missions so that they understand the state at the end of missions which gives the max points. Also, some team members (besides the coach) should be assigned to look at the Q&A pages of the FLL™ web site periodically so that any updates to missions and new "interpretations" of the rules can be shared with all other team members.

Use Reference Points
Top teams use the walls as guides whenever possible. After all, there are four sides which are fixed and can be used to help your robot navigate in a more effective manner. The typical use is with wheel guides or wall guides which travel along the wall.

The other strategy is to use mission models themselves as guides/reference points. This can be key in determining how a mission is accomplished and the type of manipulator to use. There are many ways to accomplish this, e.g. using a funnel or even a bracket on one side, etc. Even using a mission model to help the robot stop at the right location can be useful.

More Time Spent Engineering the Manipulators

A lot of missions will succeed on the effectiveness of the manipulator, so it pays to make sure you have manipulators that work at the very best. Some manipulators are not strong enough and need to be reinforced. Some manipulators need more fine tuning so that they can be more effective, e.g., better contact to target, better location on the robot, etc. Some manipulators are not appropriate for the task and need to be completely overhauled.

Simplify Path Selection

I recommend using straight line paths as much as possible, which makes the programming easier and also usually makes the solution work better. Depending on the construction of your robot, reducing the number of turns may make the mission path more predictable.

Some paths are deliberately taken to make the robot hit the side of a table and square off against that side of the table. This in effect makes the table side an intermediate point and the robot acts as if it is now starting from that side (as its new base). Intermediate points help make a complex path into one that can be managed by the robot.

Use Alignment Enhancements

I talked about the use of marks on table especially at base to help in aligning the robot before it launches from base. This helps reduce the margin of error for the mission and may help move a mission from less reliable to robust. Also, jigs should be used in alignment whenever possible, again to help reduce the error in launching from base.

Better Combination of Missions

From FLL™ 2006-7 to FLL™ 2007-8, the number of missions went from nine to 13. This means that you have to combine missions in each trip out from base in order to have the time to solve as many missions as possible. The basic strategy is to solve missions in the same area. Also, the team might want to combine missions for flow from one to the next so that completing one mission will NOT interfere with another mission in the sequence.

Emulate Nature for Best Effect

There are simple things that you can use from nature. One is that if you make a manipulator in the shape of a hand, then the grabbers should have more than one finger/tine (as in fork) on them. This serves to increase the chances that the grabber will contact the target and accomplish the mission. Of course, if the mission is to have a soft and light touch, maybe a single axle (serving as a tine) might work, but here again you can soften the contact point with the target by using any number of "soft" pieces, e.g. the axle joiner perpendicular double flexible.

Also, contact with the target needs a lot of consideration. You can make more surface contact by changing the manipulator tip from a single point end to a line or an area. This again serves to increase the margin of error to help you in the mission.

Evaluate Mission Solution over Multiple Trials

Observation and evaluation of each change to a manipulator is key in making it work better. But do not change after only one trial. Use five trials as a standard to evaluate the success. Test and observe constantly especially during the full sequence practice of a table.

Must Practice Choreography of Table Operators

Good teams have table operators who are smooth and can handle unexpected issues.

Essential
Knowledge
for
All
Team Members

"The beginning of knowledge is the discovery of something we do not understand." - Frank Herbert

The following is a briefing I give to the team members, usually during the summer, to get them ready for the season. This is just a way to get all team members on the same page and to discover if anyone needs more tutoring in some skill area. I usually let the veteran team member then work with the new members. For example, I ask a veteran member to help a new member in programming NXT-G™ during mission problem-solving and make sure it is the new member who is writing the program. This not only brings the entire team up to the same level, but also builds teamwork.

The file for this presentation will be found in the CD at the back of the book.

FLL™ Tournaments (Key Areas)

Research Presentation
Robot Performance
- Table Missions
Technical Presentation
- Hardware (robot and manipulators)
- Software (programs)
Teamwork

Basic Technical Skills

Basic understanding of differential drive robot
Navigation of robot (programming)
Understanding of mission rules
Understanding of types of missions
Understanding of types of manipulators
Understanding the problem solving process
Working with others to create initial solutions and solution adjustments
Learning how to approach problems in different ways

Basic Differential Robot

What is a differential drive robot?
- one motor on each side controlling one wheel and skid wheels in front
- both motors work together to make movement possible
- programs written must account for motors on both sides

How do we make differential drive robots work better?
- match the motors.

Navigation of the Robot
Use rotations when accuracy needed
Use timer when unsure of contact duration (usually with trigger)
Combine rotations and timer in missions for best effect
Use line follower only when line is well defined
Should use lines/table edges/mission models to help stop/guide robot or as a reference point

The Three Types of Missions
Trigger Mission
- moving to target area to hit/trigger an event
Delivery Mission
- moving token(s) from base to target area
- moving token(s) from one area to second area
- moving robot to target area
Retrieval Mission
- moving token(s) from target area to base

The Six Types of Manipulators
Shaped manipulator
Center of Gravity (COG)-based manipulator
Lever-based manipulator
Tension Trigger manipulator
Motorized manipulator
Mothership-Podship based manipulator

Shaped Manipulator
- Any shaped object that helps perform the mission.
- Can be just a stick
- Additional pieces used for support
- Best use in trigger missions

Center of Gravity (COG) Based Manipulator
- Uses COG to drop a lever
- May need additional pieces for grabbing/trapping
- Best for retrieval missions

Lever-Based Manipulator
- Uses lever to drop a load
- Needs solid contact point with target to provide effort to lever
- May need additional pieces for bucket/pivot/balance/ratchets
- Best for delivery missions, especially tokens at a height from the ground

Tension Trigger Manipulator
- Uses levers to grab/hit a load
- Contact point with target triggers event
- Usually needs lots of work and design adjustments
- Best for retrieval missions especially tokens at difficult to reach locations

Motorized Manipulator
- Uses motor to move lever/attachment
- Harder than it looks. Robot must bear weight of motor
- Needs additional pieces for bucket/pivot/balance, etc.
- Can be used in all types of missions

Mothership-Podship Manipulator
- Uses flywheel motor to capture momentum of robot mothership and move the podship with the manipulator. Saves time on missions since partially self-propelled. So far the flywheel motor is found only on one LEGO® set. Needs program that can ramp up speed from slow to fast
- Another possibility is a wind-up motor. This is found on more sets and the typical use is to wind up the motor in base, then send the robot out (MUST be outside base according to the rules), then the robot releases the wind-up motor with a manipulator OR item to deliver
- Needs work to make sure of good unhindered release from mothership
- Can be used for trigger or delivery missions

Basic Problem-Solving Process
- Understand the mission
- Plan and build initial solution
- Test and evaluate solution
- Come up with improvements
- Adapt/change/add improvements
- Repeat steps 3 to 5 until confident solution is near perfect

Techniques for Coming up with Solutions
- Analysis of past solutions
- Brainstorm with others
- Brain writing with others
- Attribute listing
- Morphological analysis
- Orthogonal thinking

At a minimum, learn to use Attribute Listing for manipulators

Past Winning Strategies
Full understanding of the rules.
- Know the state at the end of missions which give max points

Use Reference Points
- Use the walls as guides whenever possible
- Use mission models as guides/reference points

More Time Spent Engineering Manipulators
- Some manipulators not strong enough
- Some manipulators need more fine tuning
- Some manipulators not appropriate for task

Simplify Path Selection
- Use straight line paths as much as possible
- Reduce the number of turns for the robot

Use Alignment Enhancements
- Use marks on table especially in base
- Use jigs to help in alignment

Better Combination of Missions
- combine missions in similar area
- combine missions for flow from one to next

Emulate Nature for Best Effect
- Grabbers should have more than one tine/finger
- Make more surface contact by changing manipulator tip

Evaluate Mission Solution over Multiple Trials
- Test each change five times to evaluate NOT once
- Test and observe constantly

Must Practice Choreography of Table Operators
- Table operators must be smooth and able to handle unexpected issues.

Appendix

Appendix - NXT™ Pieces

LDraw™ is both a system of files and an application that can help make computer aided drawing of the LEGO® pieces.   It was developed by Jesse Jessiman, who has since passed away, but his wonderful legacy lives on with the support of many on-line contributors.

The web site is http://www.ldraw.org.

All the diagrams and instructions in this book were made possible because of LDraw™.   There were other tools involved in the rendering of the instructions, including MLCad, which stands for Michael Lachman CAD, which is an interface that uses LDraw™ files and helps to graphically drag and drop pieces in order to make 3D representations of instructions.

Here are some pieces using the LDraw™ naming convention that you might find useful:

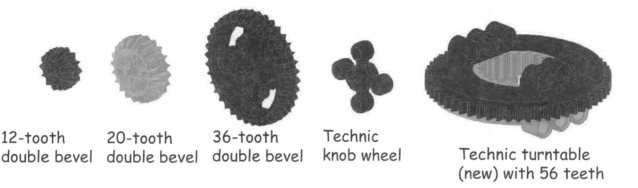

| 12-tooth double bevel | 20-tooth double bevel | 36-tooth double bevel | Technic knob wheel | Technic turntable (new) with 56 teeth |

The above pictures represent some less common gears that are found in the new NXT™ set.

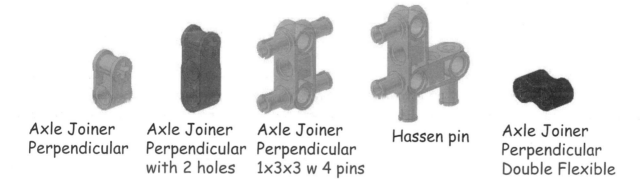

| Axle Joiner Perpendicular | Axle Joiner Perpendicular with 2 holes | Axle Joiner Perpendicular 1x3x3 w 4 pins | Hassen pin | Axle Joiner Perpendicular Double Flexible |

The above five pictures represent some common and new pieces found in the new NXT™ set. The fourth is a new piece called the Technic™ Beam 90 (3:3) with four pins.   There is an interesting story that goes along with it.   The LEGO® company decided to get some help from four users called the MINDSTORMS® User Panel. One of them, Steve Hassenplug, asked them to include a connector that would be able to connect straight liftarms at a right angle. This piece was developed, so we can nickname it the Hassen pin to make it easier to remember.   The final piece is called the Technic™ Axle Joiner Perpendicular Double Flexible and is made from rubbery material.

Appendix - Preparation for Challenges

The Challenge Mat used in the challenges is constructed from a standard size trifold display board that you can get from any office supply store.   I use Sharpie markers to make all the lines throughout the board.

The measurements for the lines and markings are all listed below.   Constructing this should only take about 15-30 minutes.   You do NOT have to be perfectly exact.   Next is buying a 2"x4" piece of wood from one of the home improvement stores. Cut the full length to give you one length about 46" long and another about 35" long.   These will form the top and left side of the border for the Challenge Mat and act as an barrier/edge.   The top-left corner is a door hinge which is secured by wood screws so that the 35" length can be folded onto the 46" length, and when the trifold board is folded, the entire Challenge Mat is very portable.

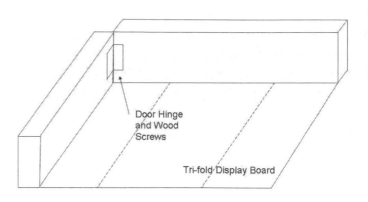

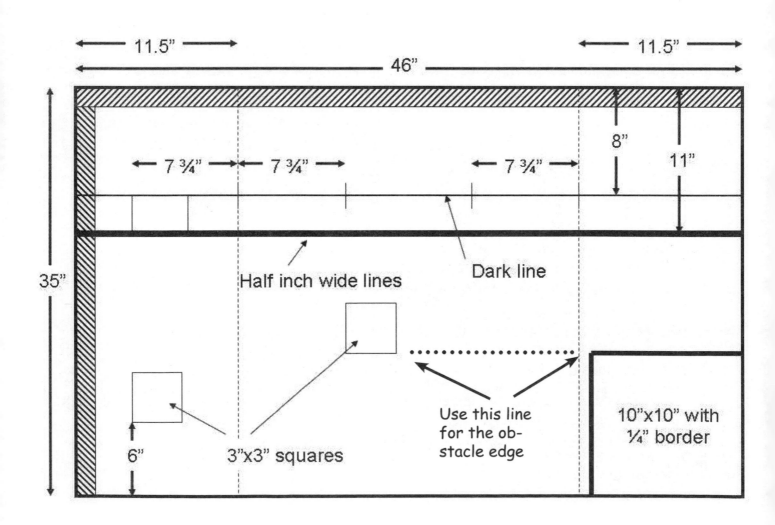

Half inch wide lines

Dark line

6"

3"x3" squares

Use this line for the obstacle edge

10"x10" with ¼" border

You now need to make some models from pieces from the sets 9797 and 9648 to be used in some of the challenges.

This is the model of the obstacle:
Light gray plate 2x8 with holes (2x)
Light gray plate 2x6 with holes (3x)

Step 1

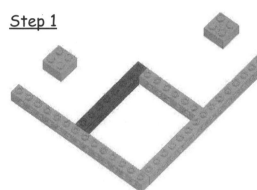

This is the model for the "In the Hole" challenge:
Light gray beam 1x16
Light gray beam 1x14
Light gray beam 1x8
Light gray beam 1x6
Light gray brick 2x2 (2x)
Some pieces are colored dark gray for contrast

Step 2

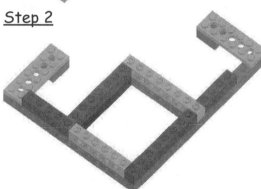

Light gray beam 1x8 (3x)
Light gray beam 1x6
Light gray beam 1x4 (2x)
Light gray plate 2x6 with holes (2x)

Step 3

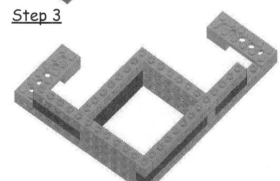

Light gray beam 1x12 (2x)
Light gray beam 1x6
Light gray beam 1x4 (2x)

Make the five tokens of the 24-tooth gear with axle 4 and one from the two Technic Triangles and two axle 8s, as shown on the right.

Appendix - Details of Other Drive Systems

The Dual Differential Drive

This drive system means that there are two differential gears used in the robot. There are two versions of dual differential drives. Both basically use the idea that one motor will control only the forward and backward motion and a second motor will control the right or left motion. Though I have seen many examples of RIS™ based dual differential drives, I have not seen any NXT™ based dual differential drives employed at FLL™ competition. I believe this is mostly because most teams have had a tougher time making RIS™ robots go forward and backward in a straight line and dual differential drives help to solve this issue. However, there is less of a problem going forward and backward in a straight line using the NXT™ based system.

Advantages
Medium difficulty to build.
Will go in a perfectly straight line unless some friction is affecting the gears or the wheels.
Also, will turn right or left.

Disadvantages
Uses lots of gears (15+) so there is a lot of resistance, hence less power to the wheels.
Also, motion, whether forward or backward or right and left is powered by one motor only so it is relatively weaker. This means the manipulator or deliverable items must be smaller or lighter.

Notes on the building of dual differential drives can be found on the next two pages. My research shows basically two versions of the dual differential drive. One version has the two differential gear shells pointing with the 16-tooth gears on the same side. The second version has both differential gear shells pointing in opposite directions.

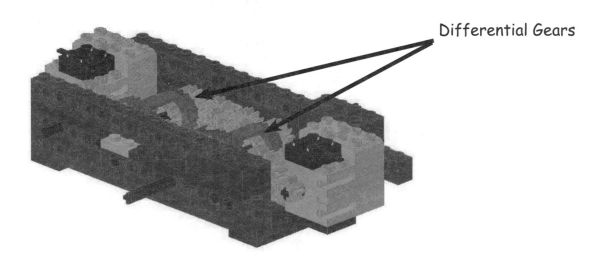

Differential Gears

In the picture with the two differential gears exposed, we see the 9V motor on the right powering the primary differential gear and controlling the forward and backward motion. The motor on the left controls the secondary differential gear and controls right and left turns.   See details in follow-up pages on the mechanisms that make this possible.

Case 1 – Primary Diff powered   VERSION 1

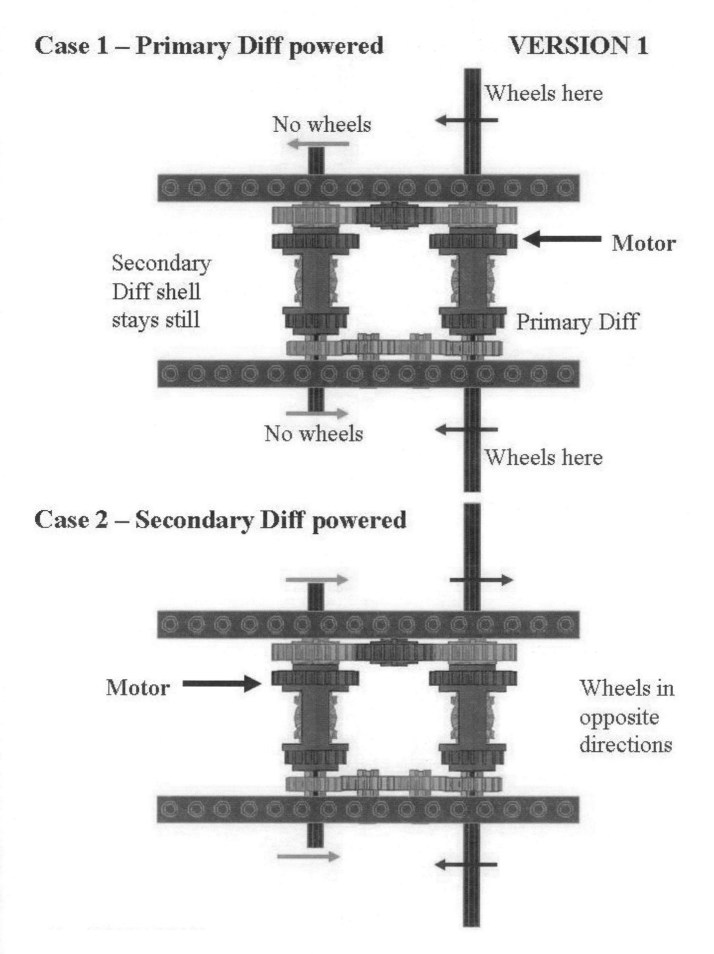

Wheels here

No wheels

Secondary
Diff shell
stays still

Motor

Primary Diff

No wheels

Wheels here

Case 2 – Secondary Diff powered

Motor

Wheels in
opposite
directions

Case 1 – Primary Diff powered   VERSION 2

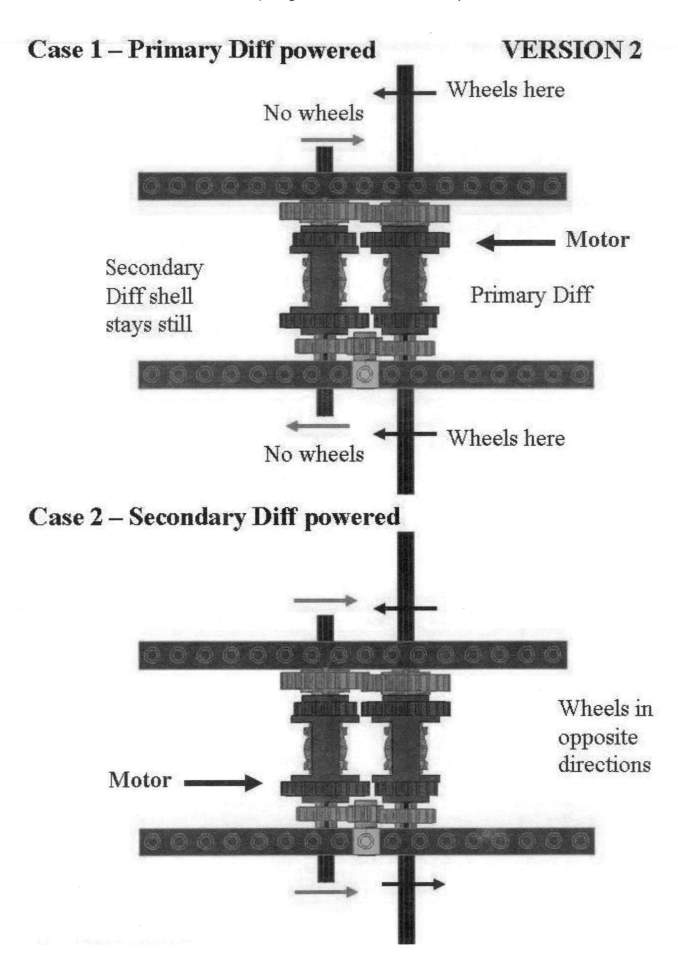

Wheels here

No wheels

Motor

Secondary
Diff shell
stays still

Primary Diff

No wheels

Wheels here

Case 2 – Secondary Diff powered

Wheels in
opposite
directions

Motor

The Skid Steer Drive

This drive system means that both sides of the robot uses treads. One implementation of this drive system uses the Wheel 43.2x22 and the Technic Treads so that it moves like a bulldozer. Steering is accomplished by skidding one or both sides.

Let us pause here and explain a pair of words - holonomic and non-holonomic - in the context of robotics. Planar motion requires two degrees of freedom in the x-axis and y-axis. Robot drive systems that allow for motion along either or both of the x-axis and y-axis are holonomic. Differential drive systems and dual differential drive systems are holonomic. However, simple skid steering without any sensors to track position is non-holonomic, because it the skidding action that causes both translation and rotation motion simultaneously. This means less predictable robot motion, especially in turning motion.

Advantages
Fairly simple to build and implement.

Disadvantages
Likely NOT to go in a straight line unless rotation is tracked and adjusted.
Turning the robot can also be an issue, as the sliding of the tracks makes it less predictable.

Example of Skid Steer
Robot using NXT™

The Synchro Drive

This drive system means all the wheels of the robot are synchronized (usually by using turntables) so that they will point (or be at an angle) in the same direction. In other words, if one wheel turns at a 45-degree angle, all wheels turn at that same angle.

This drive system is so complex, I consider it beyond the capability of most teams. This drive system is holonomic, and if implementation is correctly done, almost guarantee straight line motion. However, the builder should be careful about wheel alignment, which will affect the motion.

Advantages
Good steering and handling capabilities. This drive system is holonomic.

Disadvantages
Very hard to build and implement. Needs lots of pieces (like the old Technic™ turntable). Synchro drive system robots tend to be larger in size (so this affects the length and width) because of the large number of pieces needed and the placement of motors in that system.

Here is a picture of a synchro drive train on a robot made by Doug Carlson, which can be found at the link http://www.visi.com/~dc/synchro/index.htm

Example of Synchro Drive Robot using RIS™

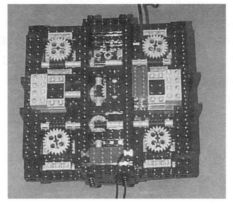

Other Drive Systems

The Car-Type Drive System

This kind of drive system is found in cars and is basically a set of driving wheels (front wheel drive or rear wheel drive) and a pair of steering wheels. Sometimes you have just one steering wheel, so it is called a tricycle. Car drive systems are non-holonomic and cannot make a rotation motion without some kind of translation motion. Needless to say most robots do not have car type drive systems.

Articulated Drive System

This kind of drive system is harder to describe but easy to understand when you see it. Basically, there are two parts to the vehicle, with a set of wheels on each, and there is a joint in the middle which can pivot with some freedom. The turning or steering is then executed when one side pinches together. This is also non-holonomic. You see this kind of drive system in some construction equipment. There is a LEGO® Technic™ set called the Front End Loader with this drive system.

Pivot Drive System

This type exist but may not be commonly found in the real world. There is a section with four wheels that are fixed and not able to pivot and there is a rotating platform which can be raised above the contact point of the wheels or lowered so that it pushes the wheels off the ground and then rotates to the correct direction. This is a holonomic drive system, and in fact the types of wheels guarantee straight line motion. However, the implementation can be hard and lots of work will need to go into the control systems. Also, this robot will not allow any kind of radius turns, as all motion will be defined in straight lines.

Useful Forms for FLL™ Missions

"To reach something good it is very useful to have gone astray, and thus acquire experience." - Saint Teresa of Avila

Mission:

Program Name:

Manipulator Location on Robot:

Sketch for Manipulator

```
┌─────────────┐
│             │
│             │
└─────────────┘

┌─────────────┐
│             │
│             │
└─────────────┘

┌─────────────┐
│             │
│             │
└─────────────┘

┌─────────────┐
│             │
│             │
└─────────────┘

┌─────────────┐
│             │
│             │
└─────────────┘

┌─────────────┐
│             │
│             │
└─────────────┘

┌─────────────┐
│             │
│             │
└─────────────┘
```

F=Forward, B=Backward, TL=Turn Left, TR=Turn Right

Listing of General Questions for Team Members on Mission Solving

Questions on the Robot Design
What kind of robot will you use?
What features do you want to see in the robot?
Which wheels will you use for your robot?
How fast does your robot need to go?

Questions About Path Selection
How do you get the robot to the target?
Does the path consist of forward and backward motion or are turns involved?
What are good ways of simplifying the path to target?
What edges/walls can you use as a reference/guide?
Will this path interfere with another mission? How can we avoid that? What is the path from the base to the target?
       Draw lines from base to targets.

Questions on Missions
What type of mission is it?
What kind of program will you need to create for the mission?
What type of manipulator do you think you need?

For the Use of Sensors
Do you need any sensors?
If so, what kind and what kind of readings do you need to make the sensors work?

Attribute Listing for Manipulators

◊ Dimensions – length, width, height (increase/decrease)

◊ Weight - payload (increase/decrease)

◊ Attachment Point to Robot (right/left, front/back, top/bottom, at an angle)

◊ Sensor triggers attachment (yes/no)
   If yes, will you use a light sensor/touch sensor/ultrasonic sensor?

◊ Impact with Target (hard/soft)

◊ Contact Place on Target (right/left, front/back, top/bottom, at an angle)

◊ Contact Region with Target (point, line, area)

◊ Center of Gravity (robot and manipulator)

◊ Friction on contact with the manipulator (more/less)

◊ Other _____

◊ Other _____

Morphological Analysis Table

	Adapt	Modify	Duplicate	Add to	Increase	Decrease	Substitute	Rearrange	Reverse	Combine	Yes / No	Switch Side	Take apart
Length													
Width													
Height													
Weight													
Attachment Point to Robot													
Sensor Triggers Attachment													
Impact with Target													
Contact Place on Target													
Contact Region with Target													
Path to Target													
Center of Gravity													
Friction on Contact with Manipulator													

Form for Checking Mission Time and Transitions

0 s	Mission Runs	Time(s)	Notes
	Mission -		
m. s.			
	Time in Base		
m. s.			
	Mission -		
m. s.			
	Time in Base		
m. s.			
	Mission -		
m. s.			
	Time in Base		
m. s.			
	Mission -		
m. s.			
	Time in Base		
m. s.			
	Mission -		
m. s.			
	Time in Base		
m. s.			
	Mission -		
m. s.			
	Time in Base		
m. s.			
	Mission -		

Date: _____
Season: _____

Date of birth: _____

Team : _____
Team number: _____

Team member: _____

<u>Goals for the Season</u>

1. _____

2. _____

3. _____

E - Exceeds Expectations, M - Meets Expectations
W - Working to Achieve Appropriate Level, N - Needs Improvement

Skills	Assessment Date:	Assessment Date:	Assessment Date:	Assessment Date:	Assessment Date:	Assessment Date:
Building Skills (robot hardware)						
Building Skills (manipulators)						
Programming Skills						
Teamwork Skills						
Research Skills						
Presentation Skills						
Problem Solving Skills						

Reference:
Higgins, J.M. (1998). *101 Creative Problem Solving Techniques* Florida: Warner Business Books.
von Oech, R. (1998). *A Whack on the Side of the Head*. New York: Time Warner Book Group.

Useful web sites:
http://www.firstlegoleague.org

http://www.fll-freak.com

http://www.legoeducation.com

http://mindstorms.lego.com

http://www.nxtprograms.com

http://www.thenxtstep.blogspot.com

What You Will Find on the Enclosed CD

I have compiled the following items that I hope you will find useful.

There are movie files either in AVI (Windows Media Player) or MOV (Quicktime) file format, which have examples of mission solutions from previous FLL™ years performed by Mech Masters team members.

There are files of example manipulators that we have used to solve missions in previous years. Note that most of these examples will require special LEGO® pieces not found in the sets 9797 and 9648.

The "Essential Knowledge for All Team Members" briefing will be in its own folder.

All the useful forms are in separate files in the CD as Master Sheets for printing.

BasicBot instructions are also found in color on the CD.